CIRIA C741

Environmental good practice on site guide (fourth edition)

Edited by
Philip Charles, CIRIA
Philip Edwards, Responsible Solutions Ltd

Griffin Court, 15 Long Lane, London, EC1A 9PN
Tel: 020 7549 3300   Fax: 020 7549 3349
Email: enquiries@ciria.org   Website: www.ciria.org

Environmental good practice on site guide (fourth edition)

Charles, P, Edwards, P (editors)

CIRIA

CIRIA C741   RP996   © CIRIA 2015   ISBN: 978-0-86017-746-3

First printed C502, 1999, reprinted 2000, 2001, 2002

Revised C650, 2005, C692, 2010

British Library Cataloguing in Publication Data

A catalogue record is available for this book from the British Library

Keywords
Construction materials and products, construction process and management, construction resources and waste management, environmental management, regeneration and contaminated land, sustainability and the built environment, sustainable water management

Reader interest	Classification	
Construction process, contaminated land, environmental management, materials, performance measures, planning, procurement, risk and value management, sustainability, waste management	Availability Content Status Users	Unrestricted Advice/guidance Committee-guided Construction professionals and managers

Published by CIRIA, Griffin Court, 15 Long Lane, London, EC1A 9PN, UK

Summary

Environmental impacts will arise at any construction project, irrespective of the location, size or nature of the development, and have the potential to affect the immediate neighbour, and also the natural and built environment. Impacts can take many forms, such as noise or pollution, and can affect surrounding flora and fauna. Good environmental practice enables these issues to be managed positively.

The task of preventing impacts or minimising the risk of potential impacts is becoming increasingly the responsibility of site-based staff. This greater accountability at site level demands higher standards of environmental awareness and education by all site staff. Though training and using experienced staff, environmental issues can be effectively managed with the speed and urgency that is often required.

This guide is a user-friendly reference tool and training aid, which provides practical advice about managing construction on site to minimise environmental impacts. It is relevant to all concerned within the construction process.

Robust project planning and a collaborative approach enables environmental issues to be positively managed. The whole project team and construction supply chain have responsibilities for good environmental management.

Good environmental practice starts with planning for good site management.

The guide is divided into four chapters:

Chapter 1 Environmental benefits and obligations

- outlines the link to sustainability
- outlines those obligations that a site operates under in terms of both legislative and contractual conditions
- presents the reasons for adopting good environmental practice on site
- introduces several emerging issues for future consideration.

Chapter 2 Project activities

- identifies the environmental issues that need to be considered when carrying out the various pre-construction, construction, post-construction activities, and also other project-based considerations.

Chapter 3 General project management

- explains how the overall establishment and management of the site forms the basis of environmental good practice
- covers management responsibility, from the initial set up of the site through to project completion and demobilisation as recognition of the projects whole life cycle.

Chapter 4 Environmental issues

- advice on how to manage impacts for a range of environmental issues. Each issue includes an introduction to the topic highlighting its importance, followed by guidance and sources of further guidance, and an overview of current legislation
- guidance is supported by legal examples, case studies, photographs, diagrams and good practice checklists.

The appendices provide lists of useful contacts including for the UK environmental regulators, and information on regulatory pollution prevention guidance (UK-wide), advisory notes (Wales) and advice notes (Scotland).

Further information to support that provided in the guide including links to further guidance, site-based toolbox talks and legislation are provided on the dedicated environmental good practice web page: **www.ciria.org/egpos**

Acknowledgments

This fourth edition has been undertaken by Responsible Solutions Ltd under contract to CIRIA, and in collaboration with a project steering group (PSG) of industry practitioners. CIRIA would like to acknowledge those involved in the development of the first edition in 1999 (C502), the second edition in 2005 (C650) and the third edition in 2010 (C692).

Project steering group

CIRIA wishes to express its thanks to the members of the group for their contributions to the guide:

Gareth Brown (chair)	WRAP (chair second and third PSG)
Nicola Ashworth	Parsons Brinckerhoff
Simon Attwood	ISG Construction
Iain Casson	Kier (formerly Barhale plc)
Helen Denham	Mott MacDonald
Martin Gettings	Canary Wharf Contractors Limited
Dr Martin Gibson	Temple Group Ltd
Dr Eva Gkenakou	Brookfield Multiplex Europe
Dr Liz Howe	Natural Resources Wales
Judith Johnston	Northern Ireland Environment Agency
Kris Karslake	BAM Construct UK Ltd
Peter Kelly	ISG Construction (formerly Sir Robert McAlpine)
Andrew Kinsey	Mace Group Ltd
Rob McCarthy	Laing O'Rourke
Ian McCauley	Northern Ireland Environment Agency
Colin Moorcroft	Skanska UK plc
Alison Morrissy	ISG Construction
John O'Reilly	Kier
Amit Patel	Galliford Try plc
Adam Spencer	Defence Infrastructure Organisation
Andrew Swain	Lafarge Tarmac
Simon Tranter	Willmott Dixon Interiors Limited
James Vance	Travis Perkins plc
Andrew Wallace	Scottish Environment Protection Agency
Vicki Walsh	GB Building Solutions (formerly Sir Robert McAlpine (chair, first PSG)
Steve Wenham	Environment Agency
Daniel Whiteley	BAM Nuttall Ltd

Technical experts

Diane Booth	Global Environmental Futures Ltd
Jay Carver	4AD Consultants
Susan Harris	SRS Sustainable Business
Graham Parry	ACCON UK Limited
John Newton	The Ecology Consultancy
Naomi Warr	Stockton Warr

Other contributors

Liz Holford	Action Sustainability
Dr Shamir Ghumra	Responsible Solutions Ltd
Betti Moser	April Textworks
Paul McCullough	Craigavon Borough Council
Ian Nicholson	Responsible Solutions Ltd
Ann MacSween	Historic Scotland
James Upstill-Goddard	Responsible Solutions Ltd

CIRIA would also like to thank 4AD Consultants, EnviroCentre, Chartered Institute for Archaeologists, HR Wallingford, Mott MacDonald, Royal Haskoning DHV, Swindon Borough Council, Temple Group and The Ecology Consultancy for providing initial comments on the environmental issues section.

SEPA

Graham Applegate, Fiona Donaldson, Mark Heggie, Punam Khaira, Jo Long, Anne Marsden, Scot Mathieson, Caroline Thornton.

NIEA

Bob Davidson, Keith Finegan, Paul Logue, Declan Looney, Paul McAnulty, Andrew McIntosh, Pamela Patterson, Rachel Patterson, Catherine Snijder, Allison Townley.

Source materials

CIRIA would like to acknowledge the following organisations with respect to the content of case studies within the guide:

Alun Griffiths (Contractors) Ltd, Amey, Balfour Beatty, Barhale Trant Utilities, Black & Veatch, Carlow Precast, Costain, Galliford Try plc, Jacobs Engineering UK Ltd, Kier, Kier Living, Laing O'Rourke, Lend Lease, London Underground, Mace Group Ltd, Mott MacDonald, Parsons Brinckerhoff, Taylor Woodrow-BAM Nuttall Joint Venture, Willmott Dixon.

CIRIA would like to thank the following organisations for providing figures (diagrams and photographs):

Arup, Balfour Beatty, BAM Nuttall, Brookfield Multiplex Europe, Bureau Veritas, Galliford Try plc, the Green Construction Board, J Murphy and Sons Ltd, Keltbray, Kier, Laing O'Rourke, Lend Lease, Mace Group Ltd, Museum of London and Archaeology (MoLA), Mott MacDonald, Parsons Brinckerhoff, Richard Saunders, Scottish Natural Heritage, SEPA, Skanska.

CIRIA Project manager

Philip Charles

Project funders

BAM Nuttall Ltd
Brookfield Multiplex Europe
Canary Wharf Contractors Limited
Galliford Try plc
Kier
Lafarge Tarmac
SEPA
WRAP
CIRIA Core member programme

Contents

Case studies

Figures

Tables

Glossary

Abatement notices A local authority has a duty under legislation to serve an abatement notice where it is satisfied that a statutory nuisance exists. The powers of an abatement notice include being able to stop work on the project.

Abstraction The removal of water from groundwater or surface waters, either temporarily or permanently. Abstraction permits/licences are required from the local regional environmental regulator.

Asbestos Banned material due to severe health implications associated with exposure. Found in many buildings as insulation material, fire retardant, used in floor and ceiling tiles, gaskets etc. Requires specialist removal and disposal by licenced organisations. Asbestos survey required when presence is suspected before demolition.

Biodiversity A term used to describe the variety of living things on earth. Maintaining or increasing biodiversity is a positive outcome.

Brownfield site As opposed to a 'greenfield' site, a brownfield site is a generic term for land used previously for an industrial or commercial purpose, being available for redevelopment towards new industrial, commercial or residential use. The level of remediation or clean-up necessary may vary significantly.

Chain of Custody Evidence that the material used in a final product has been sourced from a certified sustainable supplier. This demonstrates traceability throughout the supply chain.

Climate change The consequences upon the naturally occurring greenhouse effect arising out of man's industrial and domestic practices. There is accepted evidence that man's influence upon climate change is a reality.

Consent/licence/ permit (discharge to water) In England and Wales any intended discharge to 'controlled waters' will require permission from the environmental regulator over granting of an environmental permit. Any intended discharge to the water environment in Scotland will require permission from the Scottish Environment Protection Agency (SEPA) for granting a Controlled Activity Regulation (CAR) point discharge license. See *Trade effluent consent* for discharge to sewers.

Controlled waters/ water environment Almost all natural waters in the UK. This includes surface water (rivers, streams, lakes, reservoirs, ditches, ponds), including those temporarily dry, and groundwater (aquifers), as well as coastal waters up to three miles out. It is an offence to pollute such waters. Responsibility for policing controlled waters is placed with the regulators.

Contaminated land Land that meets the Part IIA/Part III definition of contaminated, being *"any land that appears to the local authority in whose area it is situated to be in such a condition by reason of substances in, on or under the land, that:*

	1 Significant harm is being caused or there is a significant possibility of such harm being caused
	2 Pollution of controlled waters is being or is likely to be caused."
Dust	Airborne solid matter up to about 2 mm in size. Along with noise and odour, dust is probably the most commonly complained about issue or 'statutory nuisance' from construction sites.
Duty of care for waste	A legal responsibility to ensure that production, storage, transporting and disposal of business waste is carried out without harming the environment.
EU Ecolabel	European award for products and services that meet the highest environmental standards.
Ecology	All living things, such as trees, flowering plants, insects, birds and mammals, and their habitats.
Enforcement notices	In England, Wales, Northern Ireland and Scotland, the environmental regulator has the power to serve a works notice/ consent on a site to prevent or remedy water pollution. Such notices/ consents can be served before pollution has occurred if, in the opinion of the environmental regulator, a polluting substance is likely to enter surface waters or groundwater. The environmental regulator may serve a works notice/consent to ensure that waters are cleaned up after pollution has occurred.
Environmental permit (water)	Any intended discharge to 'controlled waters' in England and Wales will require permission from the Environment Agency over granting of an environmental permit. See *Trade effluent consent* for discharge to sewers.
Environmental aspect	Element of an organisations activities or products or service that can interact with the environment.
Environmental impact	Any change to the environment, whether adverse impact or beneficial, wholly or partially resulting from an organisation's environmental aspects.
Environmental indicator	A measure of an environmental parameter, which can be used to assess the present state of the environment by looking at trends over time.
Environmental management plan (EMP)	An EMP is a project-specific plan developed to ensure that all necessary measures are identified and implemented in order to protect the environment and comply with environmental legislation. The coverage on an EMP is wider than just site-level as it can refer to decisions made before works start (eg designing out waste). Possible alternatives include Construction Environmental Management Plan (CEMP) or Site Environmental Management Plan (EMP).
Environmental receptor	Any feature, habitat, area or living organism that potentially can be negatively affected by site activities.
European Waste Catalogue Codes/ List of Waste (LoW) Codes	Codes to identify various types of waste, for example Cat. 17 02 01 Wood.

Forest Stewardship Council	An organisation that sets out international standards for the responsible management of forests in accordance with ecological, social and economic criteria.
Greenhouse gases	Naturally present and man-made gases, which contribute to the greenhouse effect. These gases include carbon dioxide, methane, and chlorofluorocarbons (CFC's).
Greywater	Lightly contaminated water captured and reused for a second purpose, eg water from wash basins used to flush toilets.
Groundwater	Water beneath the ground's surface.
Groundwater source protection zones	Zones where there is a risk of contamination from any activities that might cause pollution in the area. The closer the activity is to the source, the greater the risk. Used in conjunction with the groundwater protection policy to set up pollution prevention measures in areas that are at higher risk, and to monitor the activities of potential polluters nearby.
Heritage bodies	These bodies have a general duty to conserve heritage, to carry out scheduling of historic remains, and to undertake research. They comprise Historic England, Cadw, Historic Scotland and the Northern Ireland Environment Agency (NIEA).
Landfill tax	A tax payable to HM Revenue and Customs (HMRC) by the operator, on all waste materials going to landfill. Landfill tax from 1 April 2014 is £80 per tonne for active waste, and £2.50 for inert or inactive waste.
Local biodiversity action Plan (LBAP)	Used by local authorities and others to identify ecological objectives and targets. Aimed at ensuring sustainable development in relation to processes such as planning, the LBAP helps conserve and save valuable habitats as well as plant or animal species. LBAPs link to a national biodiversity plan set by government.
Local planning authority (LPA)	Based within local councils, the LPA is responsible for local planning issues including control of building works and development of land, protection of hedgerows and trees and listed buildings.
Mitigation	Refers to the actions and measures that may be taken to eliminate or reduce the effect of a scheme's development or operation.
Noise	Often described as being a sound that is 'not desired'. Sound is a wave motion carried by air particles between the source and the receiver (usually the ear).
Noise abatement zones	Local authorities have the power to set up a noise abatement zone as an area-based approach for controlling commercial and industrial noise.
Polluter pays principle	Also known as extended polluter responsibility (EPR) is an environmental principle that requires that polluting parties are made liable to pay for the damages they cause to the natural environment.
Pollution	Any emission as a result of human activity that may: • be harmful to human health or the quality of the environment • cause offence to a human sense

	• result in damage to material property • impair or interfere with amenities and other legitimate uses of the environment.
Prescribed processes	Any activities carried out on premises, or by means of mobile plant (eg concrete crusher), capable of causing pollution to the environment. Nearly always requires a local authority or environmental regulator licence/permit.
Recycling	Collecting and separating materials from waste and processing them to produce useable products.
Remediation notice(s)	Having identified any contaminated land within its area, the environmental regulator or the local authority may serve on an 'appropriate person' such a notice, specifying what needs to be done to remediate the land and the timescale for it to be done.
Section 60 notice	Legal enforcement action issued under the Control of Pollution Act 1974 by the local authority to control noise pollution and nuisance on construction sites. If raised, the conditions must be complied with until revoked or successfully appealed against.
Section 61 consent	An agreement with the local authority issued under the Control of Pollution Act 1974 to permit activities with the potential to cause nuisance (eg noise on site to occur).
Sewerage provider	Regional wastewater utility company (Scottish Water for Scottish residential customers, and NIEA in Northern Ireland) responsible for removal and treatment of foul water/sewage.
Stakeholders	Persons or groups who are directly or indirectly affected by a project, as well as those who may have interests in a project and/or the ability to influence its outcome, either positively or negatively.
Statutory consultees	Organisations that must be consulted at the planning stage of projects. These organisations include regulators, heritage bodies and nature conservation bodies.
Statutory Nature Conservation Bodies	Natural England, Natural Resources Wales (NRW), Scottish Natural Heritage (SNH) and NIEA have regional responsibility for promoting the conservation of wildlife and natural features.
Sustainable development	*"Development that meets the needs of the present without compromising the ability of future generations to meet their own needs"* (World Commission on Environment and Development, 1987).
Sustainable timber	Wood that is obtained from a sustainably-managed forest.
Trade effluent consent	A consent that must be sought from the relevant water and sewerage company or authority before an organisation can discharge trade effluent to a public foul sewer or to a private sewer that connects to a public sewer.
Transfer document	Required as a legal evidence describing the transfer of inert and non-hazardous waste between duty-holders.
Transfer station	Facility where waste is transferred from collection vehicles to larger vehicles or onto rail or river for onward transport for disposal. Also refers to a facility that segregates waste.

Waste	Any substance or object that the holder discards, intends to discard or is required to discard: • controlled waste – household, commercial and industrial waste • directive waste – material that the producer or holder discards • inert waste – material that does not undergo any significant physical, chemical or biological transformations. Inert waste will not dissolve, burn or otherwise physically or chemically react, eg clean bricks or concrete • non-hazardous waste – material that does not have any significant hazardous properties, but is not inert and could cause problems if not dealt with properly due to the fact it may biodegrade, eg paper, cardboard or plastic • hazardous/special waste – can be harmful to the environment and human health so cannot be disposed of by conventional methods, eg paints, solvents, oil and pesticides.
Waste minimisation/ resource efficiency	The reduction of waste at source by understanding and changing processes to minimise its production. It includes the substitution of less environmentally harmful materials in the production process.
Wildlife corridor	A linear habitat, or range of habitats in which species can survive, and along which they can move to other wildlife areas. Examples include rivers and streams, hedges and shelterbelts, field and road margins.
Works notice	See *Enforcement notices*.

Acronyms and abbreviations

A&I	Aspects and impacts
AGL	Aggregates Levy
ANC	Association of Noise Consultants
AONB	Area of Outstanding Natural Beauty
ASBP	Alliance for Sustainable Building Products
ASSI	Area of Special Scientific Interest (Northern Ireland)
BCT	Bat Conservation Trust
BIM	Building Information Modelling
BOT	Build-operate-transfer
BPM	Best practicable means
BRE	Building Research Establishment
BREEAM	Building Research Establishment Environmental Assessment Method
BS	British Standard
BTU	Barhale Trant Utilities
Cadw	Welsh Historic Monuments
CAR	Controlled Activity Regulation
CBM	Cement bound material
CCL	Climate Change Levy
CCS	Considerate Constructors Scheme
CCTV	Closed circuit television
CD&E	Construction, demolition and excavation
CECA	Civil Engineering Contractors Association
CEMP	Construction Environmental Management Plan
CEN	European Committee for Standardization
CFCs	Chlorofluorocarbons
CHAS	Contractors Health and Safety Assessment Scheme
CIEH	Chartered Institute of Environmental Health
CIfA	Chartered Institute for Archaeologists
CIP	Construction Industry Publications
CITB	Construction Industry Training Board
CL:AIRE	Contaminated Land: Applications In Real Environments
CLR	Contaminated land report
CoC	Chain of Custody
CoPA	Control of Pollution Act 1974
COPD	Chronic obstructive pulmonary disease
COSHH	Control of Substances Hazardous to Health
CPA	Construction Products Association
CSCS	Construction Skills Certification Scheme
CSM	Conceptual site model
CWS	County Wildlife Sites
DARD	Department of Agriculture and Rural Development (in Northern Ireland)
dB	Decibel
DBFO	Design, Build, Finance and Operate

DCAL	Department of Culture, Arts and Leisure (in Northern Ireland)
DCLG	Department for Communities and Local Government
D&B	Design and build
Defra	Department of Environment Food and Rural Affairs
DOENI	Department of Environment Northern Ireland
DREAM	Defence Realm Environmental Assessment Methodology
DSR	Dark Sky Reserve
EAN	Electricity Alliance North
EAP	Environmental Action Plan
ECOW	Ecological Clerk of Works
EDOC	Electronic duty of care
EHO	Environmental health officer
EIA	Environmental Impact Assessment
EMAS	Eco-Management and Audit Scheme
EMP	Environmental Management Plan
EMS	Environmental Management System
EPR	Extended polluter responsibility
ES	Environmental statement
ETI	Ethical Trading Initiative
EU	European Union
EWC	European Waste Catalogue
FBA	Furnace bottom ash
FIR	Fairness, inclusion and respect
FSC	Forest Stewardship Council
GCN	Great crested newt
GHG	Greenhouse gas
GPLC	Guiding principles for land contamination
GRI	Global Reporting Initiative
HWCN	Hazardous Waste Consignment Note
HELM	Historic Environment Local Management
HMRC	HM Revenue and Customs
HSE	Health and Safety Executive
HVAC	Heating, ventilating and air conditioning system
IAGM	Institute of Air Quality Management
IAI	Institute of Archaeologists of Ireland
IBA	Incinerator bottom ash
IDA	International Dark-Sky Association
IFC	Issued for construction
IHBC	Institute of Historic Building Conservation
INNS	Invasive Non-Native Species
IPC	Integrated Pollution Control
ISO	International Standards Organisation
JIT	Just-in-time
KPI	Key performance indicator
LAPC	Local Authority Pollution Control
LBAP	Local biodiversity action plan
LCA	Life cycle analysis
LED	Light-emitting diode

LEED	Leadership in Energy & Environmental Design
LLFA	Lead Local Flood Authority
LNR	Local Nature Reserve
LoW	List of Wastes
LPA	Local planning authority
LPG	Liquefied petroleum gas
MDF	Medium density fibreboard
MLP	Materials Logistic Plan
MOLA	Museum of London Archaeology
MRF	Material recovery facility
MS	Method statement(s)
MVHR	Mechanical ventilation heat recovery system
NBS	National Building Specification
NGO	Non-Governmental Organisation
NIEA	Northern Ireland Environment Agency
NNR	National Nature Reserve
NORM	Naturally occurring radioactive material
NRW	Natural Resources Wales
NSA	National Scenic Area (Scotland)
NVQ	National Vocational Qualification
PAN	Planning Advice Note (Scotland)
PEFC	Programme for Endorsement of Forest Certification
PFA	Pulverised fuel ash
PFI	Private Finance Initiative
PLC	Permits/licenses/consents
PPC	Pollution Prevention and Control
PPE	Personal protective equipment
PPG	Pollution Prevention Guidelines
PPP	Polluter pays principle
PSG	Project steering group
PSNI	Police Service Northern Ireland
PVC	Polyvinyl chloride
RA	Recycled aggregate
RAMSAR	Wetlands of international importance
RAP	Recycled asphalt planings
RCA	Recycled concrete aggregate
REACH	Registration, Evaluation, Authorisation and Restriction of Chemicals Enforcement Regulations 2008 (as amended)
RIGS	Regionally Important Geological Sites
RMP	Resource Management Plan
RSPB	Royal Society for the Protection of Birds
SAC	Special Area of Conservation
SEATS	Site Environmental Awareness Training Scheme
SEMP	Site Environmental Management Plan
SEPA	Scottish Environment Protection Agency
SIC	Standard Industrial Classification
SINC	Site of Importance for Nature Conservation
SLINC	Site of Local Importance for Nature Conservation

SLNCI	Site of Local Nature Conservation Importance
SMC	Scheduled monument consent
SNCI	Sites of nature conservation interest
SNCO	Statutory Nature Conversation Organisation
SNH	Scottish Natural Heritage
SPA	Special Protection Area
SSSI	Sites of Special Scientific Interest
SuDS	Sustainable drainage systems
SWMP	Site waste management plan
TAN	Technical Advice Note (Wales)
TMP	Traffic management plan
TPO	Tree Preservation Order
UEA	University of East Anglia
UXO	Unexploded ordnance
VSU	Victoria Station Upgrade
WAC	Waste acceptance criteria
WAP	Waste acceptance procedures
WEEE	Waste Electrical and Electronic Equipment
WHS	World Heritage Site
WSI	Written Scheme of Investigation
WTN	Waste Transfer Note
WRAP	Waste and Resources Action Programme

How to use this guide

This guide provides advice on environmental good practice for each construction stage and is aimed primarily at site-based staff including subcontractors, and applicable to all levels of construction.

The guide is intended to be a reference book and a training aid. A companion pocket book (CIRIA C715) presents key advice on working on construction sites, and is specifically designed to be given to site-based staff as a reference aid.

The content of this guide provides the basis of CIRIA's one-day environmental good practice on site training course.

Adoption of the good practice presented in this guide by a broader group of construction professionals could have a significant effect on construction activities and the ability of site-based staff to meet their legislative and contractual obligations to the environment.

Such professionals include:

- construction planners within contractors' main offices
- contractors
- project managers/directors
- designers
- developers
- local authority engineers
- construction managers
- quantity surveyors
- planning supervisors and principal contractors
- environmental regulators.

Use this guide with:

- Pollution Prevention Guidelines (PPG) 6, which provides practical advice and guidance to help in preventing pollution (EA, NIEA, SEPA, 2012).
- Toolbox talks produced by CIRIA on behalf of the Civil Engineering Contractors Association (CECA), BUILD UK and Construction Industry Publications (CIP), which concentrate on the issue or construction activity most relevant to the work taking place at any given time.

Links to access PPG6 (and others related to construction) is given in **Appendix A3**, and copies of the site-based toolbox talks are available from **www.ciria.org/egpos**

Throughout the guide the following symbols are used alongside the text to help identify the type of information being presented:

Case study	Key guidance	Take note

Legal example	Checklist	Further information	Plan ahead

The reader should be clear about the scope of the guide. In particular:

- it is not a health and safety manual
- it should not replace contact with regulators
- although it gives an overview of current legislation, detailed guidance should be sought from the company's environmental representative (or external specialists) if it is required
- it does not deal with environmental issues that should have been covered during the planning and design of the project, but does provide advice on how to manage these issues at the site level.

Generally, the advice given in the guide is relevant for all types of contract conditions, eg traditional, design and build (D&B), design-build-finance-operate (DBFO), build-operate-transfer (BOT) and Private Finance Initiatives (PFI).

This guide covers issues relating to the terrestrial environment. CIRIA has produced an coastal and marine environment site guide and accompanying pocket book, which are due out in 2015 (CIRIA C744 and C745).

1 Environmental benefits and obligations

This section introduces the links between environmental good practice on site and the wider agenda of sustainability within the construction industry. It also includes emerging issues for future consideration, environmental obligations and a brief description of environmental performance-based assessment schemes.

1.1 SUSTAINABLE CONSTRUCTION

'Sustainability' and 'sustainable development' are terms defined differently by different people. The original definition of sustainable development (and still most widely used), was made in the Bruntland Report (Bruntland, 1987), which defines it, as: *"Development that meets the needs of the present without compromising the ability of future generations to meet their own needs"*.

Sustainable development is crucial to the long-term development of the UK and is a principle at the highest level of national planning.

Sustainable construction is about balancing environmental, social and economic aspects. So, delivering a sustainably constructed project will contribute towards sustainable development. **Figure 1.1** demonstrates the links between environmental, economic and social aspects. It is important to be aware of all aspects of sustainable construction as clients, customers, designers and main contractors are using these aspects within sustainable policies and strategies.

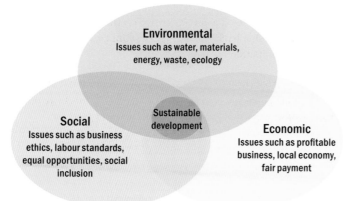

Figure 1.1   Sustainability Venn diagram

In July 2013 the UK Government released its construction strategy (HM Government, 2013), which builds on the 2008 sustainable development strategy and continues the government and construction industry's commitment to sustainability (**Figure 1.2**). The vision for this strategy is *"an industry that leads the world in low-carbon and green construction exports"*. The drivers to meet this vision are:

- improving client capability and procurement
- building a low-carbon construction industry
- understanding future work opportunities.

Figure 1.2   Construction 2025 Vision

This guide is largely focused on environmental good practice, but also considers social and economic aspects of sustainable development. The adoption of good practice in relation to environmental management can deliver several benefits through sustainable development (see also **Section 1.2**), for example:

Environmental benefits

- reduced demand for resources through better:
    - material selection, ie greater use of recycled and reclaimed

- ○   procurement, ie sustainably sourced
- ○   management, ie less waste
- reduced greenhouse gas (GHG) emissions realised through efficient design
- adopting good practice during the construction phase (eg sustainable procurement of and efficient use of resources).

Social benefits

- reduced nuisance to neighbours by adopting best practicable means (BPM) to reduce noise, dust, vibration and light pollution
- liaising with the local community before and during the project to keep them informed about works that could affect them
- increased knowledge/skills for site based-staff learning and adopting good practices
- increase in local skills through employment (eg of apprentices) that can lead to longer-term common growth.

Economic benefits

- less money wasted on fines for non-compliance with legislation and associated costs of clean-up, legal fees and management time and damage to reputation
- cost savings through improved energy efficiency, resource efficiency and carbon management.

1.2   EMERGING ISSUES

The emerging issues described below are either government or industry-led and included for two reasons:

1   They have yet to become fully established within the industry.

2   They have not yet filtered down to the target audience of this guide.

These emerging issues will have an increasing importance within the industry over the forthcoming years and are identified to raise awareness, so that they may be integrated into practice before they become mandatory.

Building Information Modelling (BIM)

BIM in simple terms is the compilation of a single database of fully integrated and interoperable information that can be used by all members of the design and construction team, as well as by owners or operators throughout an assets life cycle. Each element within an asset is created as an 'intelligent object' that contains a broad array of data as well as its dimensions and each of these elements 'knows' how it relates to other elements of the same project and the overall design.

Use of BIM on the Victoria Station Upgrade project

Victoria Station Upgrade (VSU) is being delivered by an integrated team of London Underground, joint venture contractor Taylor Woodrow-BAM Nuttall and designer Mott MacDonald.

Starting in 2006, VSU pushed the use of BIM far beyond anything previously attempted in the UK and set standards internationally. Use of BIM on the project predated the government strategy. Indeed, VSU was a reference point during development of BS 1192:2007 and the strategy, and remains an exemplar in terms of information model maturity.

The VSU model encompasses the entire project and incorporates 18 discrete design disciplines, showing how the entire project fits together. A 'birds eye' and 'worms eye' view of the model are illustrated in Figures 1.3 and 1.4 respectively.

The BIM working process was built around:

- collaboration between the client and a federated project supply chain
- a single, unified system for data creation, management and sharing
- a co-ordinated information model.

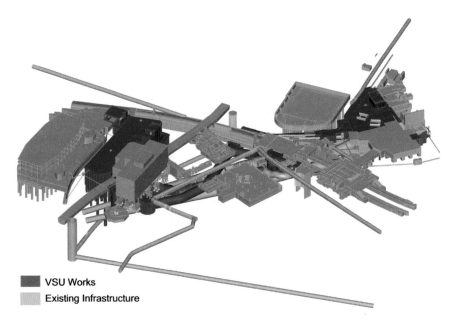

■ VSU Works
▨ Existing Infrastructure

Figure 1.3   VDU project – birds eye view (courtesy Mott MacDonald)

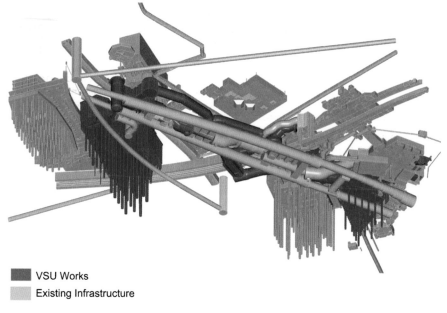

■ VSU Works

▨ Existing Infrastructure

Figure 1.4   VDU project – worms eye view (courtesy Mott MacDonald)

BIM has been identified by government as a key mechanism for getting to the heart of the construction supply chain. This is because it can help to provide better design, improve co-ordination and collaboration between all parties on a construction project and help to strip waste from key processes. Many public sector procurers and clients will begin to demand more BIM-enabled projects to deliver efficiency savings, eg through the elimination of waste.

Resource efficiency and BIM

BIM provides a digital model of the built asset, which includes information about the materials that will be incorporated into the finished asset. So, it is possible to incorporate resource efficiency into BIM. To do so, the BIM manager should:

● ensure resource efficiency is embedded within the BIM execution plan

● use an object library that is based around a standard classification system and which includes resource efficiency data (such as carbon, water and waste life cycle data) in the object parameters

● use the BIM system in a way that enables estimation and benchmarking of resource efficiency.

Sustainable procurement

Sustainable procurement is a process whereby organisations meet their needs for goods, services, works or utilities in a way that achieves value for money on a whole-life basis. It helps generate benefits not only to the organisation, but also to society and the economy, while minimising damage to the environment (Defra, 2006).

Most decisions around what to buy to deliver construction projects are made by staff based off site. These decisions are based on consideration of commercial factors, client and organisations requirements and procedures.

Those working at the site level should:

- use efficiently the materials, services, equipment and utilities that are procured for their use
- identify materials, equipment and services that provide specific sustainability benefits and provide assurance that these are achieved through, for example, correct installation. Further information about specific sustainability benefits of materials is detailed in **Section 3.2.5**
- report any quality concerns back to the procurement team.

Those based at site level such as site managers may be asked to undertake some procurement, perhaps to address an emergency (eg equipment failure on site) or to purchase low value, low risk goods or services (eg food). Sustainable procurement can be achieved by:

- checking with any procurement team if there is a 'preferred supplier' that should be used or particular guidelines that should be followed
- identifying exactly what the site actually needs
- identifying more than one potential option and compare them to determine the option providing best value for money. 'Whole life' factors should be considered, such as:
  - initial purchase price
  - speed and reliability of delivery/service
  - quality and durability
  - energy efficiency (eg electricity or battery consumption)
  - disposal costs
- considering the offerings of 'local' and smaller suppliers, as well as large companies
- purchasing only the volumes that are required.

> Failure to procure sustainably (eg timber) can result in legal non-compliance, dissatisfied clients or financial loss through reputational damage (ie resulting from materials not sustainably sourced) and challenges in securing future work.

Fairness, inclusion and respect (FIR)

The construction industry in response to government drivers (including legislation such as the Equality Act, 2010) is taking action to ensure that there is equality in the workplace. FIR is one mechanism by which this is being done by supporting the achievement of the principles of equality, diversity and anti-discrimination (**Figure 1.5**).

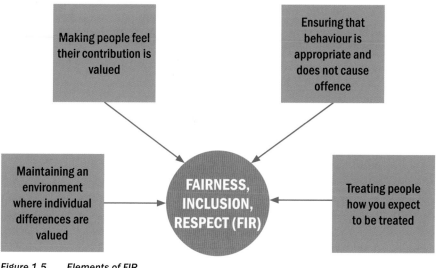

Figure 1.5   Elements of FIR

There are specific actions that site managers can undertake, so FIR is demonstrated towards and within teams, colleagues, clients and contacts (**Figure 1.6**).

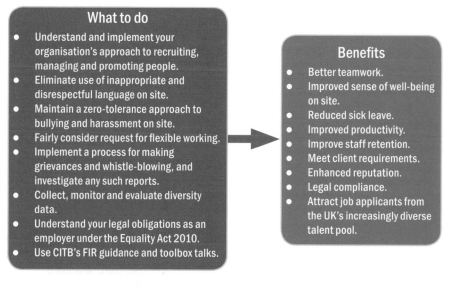

Figure 1.6   What to do to include FIR and its benefits

Failure to implement FIR can result in grievances and complaints from staff and the need to defend cases taken to industrial tribunal. It can result in reputational damage and potential loss of clients, particularly public sector organisations who have a legal obligation to promote equality.

Biodiversity/ecosystem services

Biodiversity services, also known as ecology or ecosystem services, support economic and social well-being. This includes provision of

Construction Industry Training Board (CITB) FIR guidance and toolbox talks: http://tinyurl.com/phtzkpx

food, fresh water and clean air, but also services such as protection from natural disasters, regulation of climate, water purification or pollination of crops. It is also the benefits that are perceived to come from the surrounding environment.

England, Wales, Scotland and Northern Ireland all have their own biodiversity strategy plans. While each country has variances, the basis behind all of the plans is to stop biodiversity loss, support healthy well-functioning ecosystems and establish ecological networks, and create more and better places for nature for the benefit of wildlife and people.

For example, in England, one of the priorities identified for the planning and development sector is to take a strategic view in respect to planning for nature across local areas. This approach guides development to the most appropriate locations, encourages greener design and allows the development to enhance the natural environment. It has also led to the adoption of biodiversity offsetting.

Biodiversity offsetting

Biodiversity offsetting is a conservation activity designed to give biodiversity benefits to compensate for losses, which ensure that when a development causes unavoidable damage to nature, new, larger or better nature sites will be created. These offsets differ from other types of ecological compensation as they are required to demonstrate measurable outcomes sustained over time (Defra, 2011).

Adopting this approach means that an offset provider delivers an amount of biodiversity benefit that can be quantified against that which has been lost as a result of a development. Both losses and gains are measured in the same way – even if the habitats are different.

Biodiversity offsetting does not necessarily have to been carried out by the client, designer or contractor, but can be subcontracted to another company for implementation or units of biodiversity can be purchased, similar to carbon trading schemes.

1.3 ENVIRONMENTAL OBLIGATIONS

There are many controls in place to demonstrate good practice is followed. These have both legislative and contractual origins and include:

Employer/client requirements

Contract conditions between client and developer can allow businesses to define the environmental standards that will be achieved on site during construction. They provide the opportunity to, for example, set targets, specify site resource management protocols, define scheme improvements, eg working as a 'considerate contractor', improve biodiversity and get buy-in from subcontractors. Employer/client requirements and planning conditions together form specific contractual conditions.

National environmental protection legislation

It is enforced primarily by the environmental regulators to protect both the natural environment and residents around sites. Legislation is in place to protect specific features of the environment with sites being designated and protected by virtue of their ecological, archaeological, geological or geomorphological importance.

Court convictions can lead to unlimited fines for a company and/or imprisonment or community service for the person (individual and/or appropriate director or senior manager) responsible. Liability will be more probable if it is found that suitable training, procedures or equipment were not being provided. Environmental convictions can preclude companies from tenders/ frameworks and can mean environmental permits being refused and/or revoked preventing current or future activity from being undertaken.

> Recent changes in legislation (in England and Wales) significantly raise the potential fines incurred for certain environmental offences (eg pollution incidents) that will be linked to company turnover, level of culpability and environmental harm caused. This could mean fines that were previously at the level of £10 000s could now increase to £100 000s.
>
> Added to the cost of these fines are legal, clean-up costs as well as reputational damage that could significantly affect an organisations ability to secure future work (ie being excluded from bidding for certain clients work).

Local control

Local authorities can impose several requirements through the powers given to them by national legislation including noise and air controls. Planning legislation at both a local and national level is the main control on construction development covering many aspects including scale and traffic.

Other government agencies such as the Environment Agency, Natural Resources Wales (NRW), Scottish Environment Protection Agency (SEPA), and Northern Ireland Environment Agency (NIEA) can also impose local controls.

Planning conditions can be imposed on a project through the planning system, to ensure the commitments made to the local communities are delivered, and may include provisions made after an Environmental Impact Assessment (EIA).

Corporate control

Many contractors have corporate environmental policies and an Environmental Management System (EMS) that employees are required to follow. There may be a site specific Environmental Management Plan (EMP) for a project that stipulates the necessity to identify opportunities for enhancement of the surrounding environment opposed to merely minimising potential damage. Other corporate controls include:

- company targets and objectives set through the EMS
- key performance indicators (KPIs)
- company action plans
- a sustainability policy
- signing up to external initiatives.

EMPs help to ensure that project programmes, legislation requirements and environmental projection risks and associated protection and mitigation measures are identified and achieved during project design, implementation, use and end of life. EMPs may be required as part of a company's overall EMS, under planning/ consent conditions to demonstrate, support and implement environmental commitments and requirements as well as supporting applications for biodiversity and landscape conservation, and legal agreements with environmental authorities or other interested parties.

The content of an EMP is likely to include:

1 Introduction.
2 Purpose and structure.
3 Scope of work, eg location, description of the works, construction programme, equipment and plant.
4 Environmental management framework.
5 Environmental policy.
6 Environmental aspects and impacts:
   - access routes/points
   - site housekeeping
   - water quality and drainage
   - nature conservation
   - compensation and enhancement
   - landscape design
   - noise and vibration
   - air quality
   - archaeology and cultural heritage
   - soils
   - land contamination
   - waste
   - energy
   - materials
   - transport
   - pollution prevention
   - fuel and oil handling
   - maintenance of plant

- concrete washout
- control of sedimentation

7 Legal and other requirements:
  - identification of applicable legislation and other requirements, consents and licenses
8 Objectives and targets.
9 Structure and responsibilities.
10 Training awareness and competence.
11 Communication (internal and external).
12 Operational control procedures.
  - site establishment
  - boundary fencing
  - protection of environmental features
  - emergency planning
13 Complaints, compliments and inquiries.
14 Checking.
15 Evaluation of compliance.
16 Non-conformance and corrective/preventative action.
17 Control of records.
18 Management review.

1.4 PROJECT ASSESSMENT SCHEMES

Within the construction industry there are a number of assessment schemes that are directly designed to assess the environmental performance (and aspects of social and economic performance) of projects. These schemes reflect levels of industry good practice and in performance recognition with the industry and regulatory authorities.

These schemes provide an ideal framework to demonstrate a project's environmental good practice intentions and reporting performance as well as ensuring further improvement. They do not replace the need for application of management controls, such as an EMS (see Section 3.1.7).

This section highlights some of the most commonly used schemes, but by no means all. Applying good practice from this guide, where appropriate, will further assist in demonstrating site performance.

Considerate Constructors Scheme (CCS)

CCS is an independent not-for-profit scheme designed to improve the image of construction. Sites are assessed on a variety of criteria including health and safety, environmental management and community interaction. Assessment leads to a site score and awards system. Although this is a voluntary scheme, it is increasingly required in contract conditions, including the expected score to be achieved.

CEEQUAL

CEEQUAL is the evidence-based sustainability assessment, rating and awards scheme for civil engineering, infrastructure, landscaping and works in public spaces, and celebrates the achievement of high environmental and social performance.

It aims to deliver improved project specification, design and construction of civil engineering works. CEEQUAL rewards project and contract teams in which clients, designers and contractors go beyond the legal, environmental and social minima to achieve distinctive environmental and social performance in their work. In addition to its use as a rating system to assess performance, it also provides significant influence to project or contract teams as they develop, design and construct their work, because it encourages them to consider the issues in the question set at the most appropriate time.

Building Research Establishment Environmental Assessment Method (BREEAM)

BREEAM is a series of environmental assessment schemes for buildings, developed and operated by the Building Research Establishment (BRE). There are BREEAM assessment processes and tools for different sectors (eg education, retail, offices and prisons).

New assessment tools are developed to reflect needs in the building industry and the schemes are updated to reflect industry developments and expectations. Building design and construction processes are assessed and rated to provide an overall score, which is transferred into a building rating.

Leadership in Energy & Environmental Design (LEED)

LEED is a green building certification system from the USA, providing third party verification that a building or community was designed and built using strategies aimed at improving performance across all the key metrics:

- energy savings
- water efficiency
- CO_2 emissions reduction
- improved indoor environmental quality
- stewardship of resources and sensitivity to their impacts.

Defence Realm Environmental Assessment Methodology (DREAM)

DREAM is an online environmental assessment tool for new building and refurbishment projects on defence estates.

Constructing Excellence environmental performance indicators

Constructing Excellence produces a series of environmental indicators that aim to improve the industry. These can be applied to either benchmark a site's performance against industry standards, or to set targets for improvement.

BES 6001

BES 6001 is a standard for responsible sourcing of construction products. BES 6001 provides a way for organisations, manufacturing sites or products to gain certification via a recognised auditing body. It is based on a points rating system and:

● promotes responsible sourcing of construction products

● provides clear guidance on sustainability aspects that should be addressed

● provides confidence that materials and products are being responsibly sourced.

The requirements and associated action have been structured into three components:

1 Organisational management requirements.

2 Supply chain management requirements.

3 Requirements related to the management of sustainable development.

Ethical Trading Initiative (ETI)

The ETI is an independent alliance of companies, trade unions and voluntary organisations that promote improved conditions for workers in global supply chains. ETI have established a series of Base Code Principles to which members have to subscribe to and implement through their own management systems. Members are audited against these principles. The ETI provides practical tools and guidance to help with this implementation. Some of the Principles include:

● working conditions are safe and hygienic

● child labour shall not be used

● living wages are paid

● working hours are not excessive

● no discrimination is practised.

Considerate Constructors Scheme (CCS): www.ccscheme.org.uk

CEEQUAL: www.ceequal.com

Building Research Establishment Environmental Assessment Method (BREEAM): www.breeam.org

Leadership in Energy & Environmental Design (LEED): www.usgbc.org/leed

Defence Realm Environmental Assessment Methodology (DREAM): www.dreamassess.com

Constructing Excellence environmental performance indicators: www.constructingexcellence.org.uk/zones/kpizone

BES 6001: www.greenbooklive.com/search/scheme.jsp?id=153

Ethical Trading Initiative (ETI): www.ethicaltrade.org

Global Reporting Initiative (GRI): www.globalreporting.org

Contractors Health and Safety Assessment Scheme (CHAS): www.chas.co.uk

---

Global Reporting Initiative (GRI)

The GRI is an international, multi-stakeholder, not-for-profit organisation. The scheme is a disclosure framework for sustainable information and reports on a company's environmental, economic and social performance for any size, sector or location. Performance indicators, such as, economic performance, materials, energy, waste, labour management, human rights, society and product responsibility performance, can be used to report against.

Contractors Health and Safety Assessment Scheme (CHAS)

CHAS is a scheme for suppliers to demonstrate a level of health and safety competence to potential buyers and clients. The scheme assesses members':

- health and safety policy statement
- the organisation for health and safety
- the specific health and safety arrangements to a standard acceptable to buyers and to others.

1.5 FURTHER READING

BERRY, C and MCCARTHY, S (2011) *Guide to sustainable procurement in construction*, C695, CIRIA, London (ISBN: 978-0-86017-695-4). Go to: **www.ciria.org**

DCLG (2012) *National Planning Policy Framework*, Department for Communities and Local Government, London (ISBN: 978-1-40983-413-7). Go to: **http://tinyurl.com/abvfzc2** (accessed 10 November 2014)

DOENI (2014) *Strategic Planning Policy Statement for Northern Ireland*, Department of the Environment Northern Ireland (in preparation). Go to: **www.planningni.gov.uk/spps** (accessed 10 November 2014)

DOENI (2002) *Northern Ireland Biodiversity Strategy*, Department of the Environment Northern Ireland, Belfast. Go to: **www.doeni.gov.uk/nibs_2002.pdf** (accessed 12 November 2014)

GELDER, J, TEBBIT, J, WIGGETT, D and MORDUE, S (2013) *BIM for the terrified – a guide for manufacturers*, Construction Products Association (CPA) and National Building Specification (NBS), UK (ISBN: 978-1-90941-503-4). Go to: **http://tinyurl.com/o2h8tyl**

SCOTTISH GOVERNMENT (2013) *2020 Challenge for Scotland's Biodiversity*, The Scottish Government, Edinburgh (ISBN: 978-1-78256-586-4).
Go to: **www.scotland.gov.uk/Resource/0042/00425276.pdf** (accessed on 16 December 2014)

SCOTTISH GOVERNMENT (2014) *Scottish Planning Policy, Scottish Government*, Edinburgh (ISBN: 978-1-78412-567-7). Go to: **www.scotland.gov.uk/Publications/2014/06/5823** (accessed 10 November 2014)

WELSH GOVERNMENT (2006) *Environment Strategy for Wales*, Welsh Government, Cardiff. Go to: **http://tinyurl.com/qxl6944** (accessed 12 November 2014)

WELSH GOVERNMENT (2009) *One Wales: One Planet, a sustainable development scheme for Wales*, Welsh Government, Cardiff. Go to: **http://tinyurl.com/nwpdmkv** (accessed 16 December 2014)

WELSH GOVERNMENT (2014) *Planning Policy Wales, seventh edition*, Welsh Government, Cardiff (ISBN: 978-1-47341-281-1). Go to: **http://tinyurl.com/nh8udte** (accessed 10 November 2014)

1

2

3

4

Appendices

2 Project activities

At every stage of the construction process there is the potential for effects on the environment to occur. This section contains a series of checklists to highlight some of the key issues that may be associated with a range of activities carried out on site during different stages of the construction process.

The checklists are not exhaustive, but are intended to include important issues that should be considered at each activity and stage. Reference is made to other sections of this guide to provide further advice.

It is intended that the checklists are reviewed to identify those activities and issues applicable to a particular site and then used to assess during site inspections whether or not they are being managed appropriately. Following this assessment the necessary changes to site practice can be carried out.

The checklists are divided into the following activities and sub-activities. In each case the sub-activities are listed in alphabetical order.

Pre-construction phase

- project planning
- site investigation
- site establishment
- temporary works
- site clearance.

Construction phase

- brick/blockwork
- concrete batching
- concrete pours and aftercare
- crushing, screening and reuse of materials
- demolition
- dewatering
- dredging
- earthworks
- excavation
- grouting
- landscaping/re-establishment

- piling
- refurbishment of buildings
- repairs to exposed structural elements (eg bridges, soffits, cladding)
- roadworks
- superstructure
- tunnelling.

Post-construction phase

- demobilisation
- permitting
- review activities (lessons learnt and good practice)
- site handover and commissioning.

Other issues requiring consideration

- use of hand tools
- use of plant and equipment
- use of oils and chemicals
- working near water
- working with groundwater.

2.1   PRE-CONSTRUCTION PHASE

Project planning

Key issues	Section
Identifying environmental responsibilities (eg planning conditions, assessment schemes, environmental targets)	1.3
Identifying applicable legislation	1.3
Identifying the permits and/or consents and licences (eg water abstraction, water discharge, waste) required	1.3
Undertaking of an aspects and impacts assessment to identify environmental risks on and around the site	3.1.1
Defining content of the EMP that incorporates: • options for reuse of materials on or off site – forming the basis of a resource management plan (RMP) • identifying expected waste streams – forming the basis of the site waste management plan (SWMP) • emergency response procedure.	3.11 3.2

Key issues	Section
Identifying and appropriate engagement of project stakeholders, eg through leaflet drops, helpline or project website, including local community and regulators	3.3
Identifying training requirements and preparation of site inductions for site-based staff, eg toolbox talks	3.1.5
Communicating of site environmental requirements to the supply chain	3.1.4

Site investigation

Key issues	Section
Determining the scope of ecological surveys required – and whether specialist advice is required	4.1.4
Determining the scope of land contamination investigations required and whether specialist advice is required	4.3.3 4.3.4
Determining the scope of archaeological investigations required and whether specialist advice is required	4.2.3 4.2.5

Site establishment

Key issues	Section
Determining the most appropriate location for the placement of site offices and facilities	3.2
Defining storage areas for materials, fuels and oils	3.2
Defining storage area for materials to be reused on site	3.2
Defining waste facilities and facilities on site	3.2
Identifying and protecting on and offsite drainage	3.2 4.7.8
Identifying and protecting surface water and groundwater	3.2 4.7.3
Identifying all underground services before work starts	3.2
Determining the most appropriate location of vehicle wash off facilities	3.2 4.7.3
Determining the most appropriate location of concrete wash off areas	3.2 4.7.3
Determining the appropriate hoarding/site fencing required to secure the site	3.2

Temporary works

Key issues	Section
Ensuring that required permissions have been sought before any works begin, eg Section 61 consent from the local authority	4.3.3.1
Ensuring that procedures are in place to avoid pollution when carrying out works near or over watercourses	4.7.8
Ensuring potentially noisy activities, eg on-site steelwork fabrication, is carried out at an appropriate or agreed time of the day	4.4.3.4
Identifying options to reuse materials on or off site	4.5.3.6

Site clearance

Key issues	Section
Ensuring agreed procedures are in place to manage land contamination when it is discovered	4.3.4
Ensuring agreed procedures are in place and measures to protect or relocate protected species (wildlife and/or vegetation)	4.1.5
Ensuring agreed procedures are in place to deal with the discovery and removal of invasive non-native species	4.1.6
Ensuring agreed procedures are in place to deal with the removal and reinstatement of vegetation (habitat translocation)	4.1.7
Ensuring agreed procedures are in place to deal with archaeological finds (including human remains)	4.2.5
Ensuring agreed procedures are in place to manage nuisance (noise, dust and vibration) occurring during site operations, eg as a result of movement of materials	4.4.1.4 4.4.3.4
Ensuring that procedures are in place to avoid pollution when carrying out works near or over watercourses	4.7.8
Identifying options to reuse materials on or offsite, eg brickwork for hardcore	4.5.3.6 4.5.2.1
Ensuring waste is disposed of in accordance with regulations, eg waste carrier's licence	4.5.3.5 4.5.3.8

2.2 CONSTRUCTION PHASE

Brick/blockwork

Key issues	Section
Avoid unnecessary wastage of materials by: • not over-ordering materials • storing in packaging to protect them • storing away from vehicle movements • preventing ready-mixed mortar from drying out • avoiding cutting and chasing.	4.5.2.1 4.5.2.3
Reuse of excess bricks or blocks, either on or off site. If damaged use them as hardcore on site access roads, but before doing so ensure that the appropriate permit is in place	4.5.2.1 4.5.2.3
Segregate and recycle packaging waste	4.5.2.3 4.5.3.5
Reduce dust nuisance from cutting and chasing	4.4.1.4
Only carry out activities with the potential for causing nuisance during agreed working hours	3.3.1 4.4.3.4

Concrete batching

Key issues	Section
Minimise visual, noise and dust disturbance to neighbours	3.3.1 4.4.1.4 4.4.3.4
Minimise nuisance to neighbours from noise of motors and conveyors	4.4.3.4 4.4.3.5
Minimise waste and contamination of aggregates during storage	4.5.2.6
Store and dispose of additives to prevent spillage and contamination	4.5.2.6
Accurate prediction of volume required to avoid over production and waste	4.5.2.1
Potential of highly alkaline washout from mixing plant or cleaning of ready-mix concrete lorries contaminating watercourses	4.7.6
Release of concrete from concreting operations that are near or in watercourses (floating batchers)	4.7.8
Recycle returned concrete to reduce washout volumes and produce viable aggregate	4.5.2.1
Potential of alkaline cement dust released from silos during filling to harm ecology and annoy neighbours	4.4.1.2 4.4.1.4

Key issues	Section
When cleaning silos, reverse jet filters will minimise dust emissions by capturing and reusing cement dust	4.4.1.4
Prevent of overfilling and spillage from pipelines and pumps because of poor maintenance	3.4
Maintain plant well to prevent noise and emissions	4.4.1.4 4.4.3.4

Concrete pours and aftercare

Key issues	Section
Control the storage, handling and disposal of shutter oils	4.5.2.6
Use suction as opposed to blowing dust and debris out of formwork to avoid annoying neighbours	4.4.1.4
Concrete batching plant has a dust suppression system installed and a high level alarm to prevent overfilling	4.4.1.4
Carry out regular checks on ready mix concrete wagons to check for defects, in particular hydraulic hoses, especially when works are being carried out in or near watercourses	4.7.8
Identify the wastes that will be generated and plan their handling and disposal. For example concrete curing compounds (spray applications), blackjack waterproofing (silane), polyvinyl chloride (PVC) sheeting, frost protection materials	4.5.3.5
A concrete pour may displace wastewaters from the hole. These may be contaminated with sediment and cleaning materials from the side of the structure. Dispose of them appropriately	4.7.6
In or near a watercourse, control the placing of any wet concrete to minimise the risk of cement leaking into the watercourse. Shutter failure in such locations can cause major pollution in the watercourse	4.7.8
The washout from a concrete mixing plant, or and from the cleaning of ready-mix concrete lorries, is contaminated with cement and so is highly alkaline. Do not allow it to enter any watercourse or groundwater. Alternatively consider returning the wagon to the batching plant to wash out the container, ie only the chute on site to minimise wash waters on site	4.7.8
To dispose of washout water obtain consent and dispose of it to the foul sewer via a settling tank	4.7.6
Large areas of concrete can create dust when dry, so clean regularly	4.4.1.4

Crushing, screening and reuse of materials

Key issues	Section
Authorisation will be needed to operate a crusher and screener on site. An exemption for the reuse of crushed material may be required, check with regulator	3.3.1
An exemption for the reuse of crushed material may be required unless it meets the requirement of the Waste and resources Action Programme (WRAP) Quality Protocol. Check with regulator	4.5.2.3
Work within the requirements of the permit in terms of emissions, working hours and monitoring regime	3.3.1 4.4.1.4
When operating a crusher ensure it is sited away from sensitive receptors	4.4.3.4
Ensure the discharge from crushers and screens onto conveyors is enclosed as far as practicable to minimise the effects of noise and dust	4.4.1.4 4.4.3.4
Stockpiled material should be suitably covered to prevent dust arising	4.4.1.4 4.5.2.6
Road transport of screened/crushed material is sheeted/in covered wagons	4.4.1.4 4.6.1
Effective use of crushed and screened materials on site	4.5.2.1
Ensure that sampling is undertaken to meet physical (eg class 6f2 coarse grading) and chemical requirements (eg asbestos, less than one per cent of class X material)	4.5.2.1 4.5.2.3

Demolition

Key issues	Section
Locate and mark all underground pipes, tanks and services. Also label all tanks with their content and capacity. Check for any visible signs of leaking tanks or pipes, and any signs of contaminated ground or groundwater	4.7.3 4.3.4
Review the disposal options for the materials that will be generated. Reclaim and reuse materials where possible. Identify markets for materials. Segregate materials as they are generated. Label waste clearly and store in a designated area. Dispose of any materials in accordance with regulations	4.5.2.1 4.5.3.5
If materials such as concrete or masonry are to be crushed on site, ensure that any necessary licences/permit is obtained from the local environmental health officer in England, Wales and Northern Ireland, or from SEPA in Scotland	3.1.2 3.2
Before removing or perforating tanks, check that all of their contents and residues have been emptied for safe disposal by a competent operator. Pipes may contain significant quantities of oil or chemicals, and should be capped, or valves closed, to prevent spillage. Ensure suitable spill response materials and emergency instructions are available on site and that staff have been adequately trained	3.4 4.5.3.8
All asbestos should be dealt with by a registered contractor. Ensure the locations of materials containing asbestos are identified through a formal site survey before starting work	4.5.3.8

Key issues	Section
Noise and vibration may annoy neighbours. Consider screening the works and undertake monitoring if needed	3.3.1 4.4.3.4
Dust from the demolition process may annoy neighbours and damage ecology near the site. Damp down structures during demolition and undertake monitoring if needed. Ensure any runoff from the site is prevented from entering watercourses or soakaways	4.4.1.4 4.7.8
If elephant chutes are being used, ensure that each section is securely fixed, that the skip or lorry at the discharge end is covered, and that materials are dampened before being sent down the chute	4.4.1.4
Prevent dust escaping from materials in lorries leaving the site. If it is not possible to cover lorries because there are pieces of protruding material, spray them with water just before they leave	4.4.1.4

Dewatering

Key issues	Section
Discharges of dewatering effluent will require permission from the regulator	4.7.6
Sufficient area should be planned for any settlement lagoons	4.7.4
Settlement times should take account of the size of suspended solids, eg clay solids require longer settlement times than sand	4.7.4
Pumping rates should be controlled so as to avoid erosion or scouring of riverbanks/ riverbeds	4.7.4
Provision should be made to remove any oil before discharge	4.7.3 4.7.6
Discharge on to grassland may be permissible in certain circumstance	4.7.6

Dredging

Key issues	Section
Dredging's may be contaminated with substances such as oils and heavy metals. Sample and test the sediments to provide vital information for considering disposal options	4.5.3.7 4.5.3.8
Aim to reuse the dredging's, for example, to improve agricultural land, rather than disposing of them to landfill	4.5.2.1
Pre-consultation with the regulator and interested parties, eg boat clubs and riparian owners, before dredging works start	3.3
Plan the disposal of dredging's before starting works, to allow time for obtaining any permissions required under appropriate waste management licensing/permitting regulations	3.1.2 4.5.3.8
Disposing of dredging's at sea requires a licence	4.5.3.7 4.5.3.8

Key issues	Section
Dredging materials contaminated with heavy metals or oils may lead to the production of materials classified as hazardous waste, and as such appropriate disposal will be required	4.5.3.7 4.5.3.8
If landfilling the dredging's, obtain an exemption from landfill tax for dredging's arising from maintenance of navigable inland waterways	4.5.3.7 4.5.3.8
Obtain a discharge consent for returning effluent from dewatering dredging's to controlled waters	4.7.6
The dewatering sediments may cause an odour problem	4.4.1.5
Dredging may affect the aquatic ecology, so should be undertaken outside the fish spawning season. Use an appropriate dredging technique, eg dredge mats and silt curtains, to minimise the disturbance of sediment resulting in silting of the watercourse and potential mobilisation of contaminants	4.7.3
Disturbance of organic silts and dying weed may lead to deoxygenation. Monitor and aerate if necessary. Undertake outside fish spawning season	4.7.3
Working with compacted sediments may generate high levels of noise. Also, mechanical dewatering and compaction may lead to vibration	4.4.3.4

Earthworks

Key issues	Section
Minimise the surplus materials arising from earthworks by considering methods of improving the spoil, eg *in situ* stabilisation	4.5.2.1
Dispose of surplus materials arising from earthworks in accordance with legislation. Testing of the spoil may be required to provide information for considering disposal options. Aim to reuse spoil but be aware that it needs to be in accordance with planning permission, eg land profiling/raising and may need an exemption from a permit/licence	4.5.3.8
Be aware of unexpected contamination revealed during earthworks. Stop works immediately, clear the site and consult an specialist for advice	4.3.4
Be aware of unexpected archaeological finds. Materials to look out for during excavations include burned or blackened material, brick or tile fragments, coins, pottery or bone fragments, skeletons, timber joints or post holes, brick or stone foundations, in-filled ditches	4.2.5
Be aware of unexpected ecological finds, for example the presence of newts. Should any species be found stop work immediately and consult an ecologist	4.1.4
Keep water away from unsurfaced areas using measures, such as cut-off drains. Control and dispose of silty water in a controlled manner, all discharges other than clean rainwater, eg storm drainage and excavation dewatering wastewater, may require consent. Adequate treatment, eg settlement, should be provided before discharge	4.7.3 4.7.6

Key issues	Section
Earthmoving plant and vehicles used to transport materials from and around the site may cause negative impacts from emissions, mud and noise. Construct appropriate haul roads. Maintain plant and vehicles. Use road sweepers, manual sweeping, scraping and jet washing to minimise mud/debris on roads	4.4.1.4 4.4.3.4 4.6.2
Stockpiling of topsoil for reuse should be less than two metres high to prevent damage to the soil structure	4.5.2.6
Stockpiles should be positioned away from watercourses and drainage and any potential contamination from dust or runoff controlled	3.2.5 4.7.3
Minimise the potential for suspended solid generation by using a phased stripping approach reducing the amount of exposed earth	4.7.2 4.7.3

Excavation

Key issues	Section
Prevent water entering excavations. When water does enter excavations, take measures to avoid it becoming contaminated. Dispose of it correctly	4.7.5 4.7.6
Be aware of unexpected archaeological finds. Materials to look out for during excavations include burned or blackened material, brick or tile fragments, coins, pottery or bone fragments, skeletons, timber joints or post holes, brick or stone foundations and in-filled ditches. If any unexpected finds are encountered stop work immediately and consult a specialist for advice	4.2.5
If excavation reveals contamination, stop digging immediately. Clear the site immediately and where appropriate, try as far as possible to identify the extent and cause of contamination, eg spillage on site, rupture of subterranean pipeline, and attempt to contain contaminants before consulting a specialist for advice	3.4 4.3.4
If asbestos is uncovered unexpectedly during digging operations, stop digging operations at once and refill the excavation. Remove site staff immediately and secure the area. Contact site management immediately	4.5.3.8
Poorly maintained excavation plant and vehicles used to transport materials from and around the site may cause adverse effects such as from emissions, mud and noise. Service and maintain regularly and ensure vehicles are sheeted over	3.2.6 4.4.1.4 4.4.3.4 4.6.2
Use a wheel wash and road sweeper to minimise dirt on public highway	4.7.3
Spoil arising from excavation can be recycled if not contaminated. Crush any rock arising and use on or off site. Store topsoil for reuse in piles less than two metres high to prevent damage to the soil structure. Use excavated materials to form noise bunds and for landscaping – check whether planning permission/exemption is required	4.5.2.6 4.4.3.4

Grouting

Key issues	Section
Blowback from blockages or overfilling from pressure grouting with dry materials, eg cement, can cause significant dust problems. Work within an enclosure where necessary particularly when in or near sensitive areas	4.4.1.4
Grouting in or near contaminated ground may displace polluted water in the excavation. Prevent the uncontrolled release of this water	4.7.3 4.7.6
Prevent the uncontrolled discharge of cements and bentonite slurries. Use a settlement tank to remove sediments and obtain a discharge consent before releasing the effluent	4.7.4 4.7.6
Grout waste can be more successfully separated by the addition of a chemical flocculant, or by hydroclone separation or mechanical dewatering. This allows easier disposal of the constituents	4.7.4
Dispose any slurry waste (water mixed with silt) appropriately	4.7.3

Landscaping/re-establishment

Key issues	Section
Refer to the local biodiversity action plan (LBAP). It is beneficial to select a range of native species to maintain local biodiversity	4.1.4
Identify the use and location when selecting species, eg when landscaping inclines, select appropriate species mix for gradient and to help prevent soil erosion	4.1.7 4.1.8
Identify the visual impacts and maintenance requirements when designing the landscaping. This should take consideration of the local stakeholders and intended users	3.2
Consider early landscaping to offer some noise, dust and visual screening	4.4.1.4 4.4.3.4
Note that hard landscaping may increase flood risk. Ensure appropriate drainage is provided to accommodate runoff	4.7.3
Segregate and reuse excavated materials, topsoil and subsoil for use during landscaping	4.5.2.6
Identify the accidental or deliberate introduction or spreading of invasive non-native species	4.1.6

Piling

Key issues	Section
If recycled aggregates are used as the piling mat an environmental permit/ exemption would be needed for the reuse of this recycled material, and if it has not been produced in conformance to the aggregates quality protocol	4.5.2.3
Maintain plant regularly to optimise fuel efficiency	4.5.1
Minimise the risk of spillage when using oils and chemicals	3.4
Noise and vibration may annoy neighbours. The noise levels created by piling vary with the method used. Some methods will not be allowed in urban areas, or other sensitive locations where the site has immediate residential neighbours – so use the right plant	4.4.3.4
Manage bentonite appropriately to prevent its release to the environment. Recycle if possible or dispose of it properly	4.5.2.1 4.7.3
Manage wastes arising from the piling operations. Wastes from bored piling may be a particular problem as it is often wet. Dispose of this waste in a controlled manner	4.5.3.7 4.5.3.8
Piling close to watercourses, including groundwater, forms a potential pollution risk	4.7.3 4.7.8
Contaminated ground may be encountered, which could introduce a pathway that contaminants, mobilised by groundwater, may escape through. It is important to develop a contingency plan for dealing with it. If it is encountered, stop works, clear the site and consult a specialist for advice	4.3.4
Contaminated spoil should be stored separately from other materials and be disposed of according to the legislation	4.5.3.8

Refurbishment of buildings

Key issues	Section
Explore the opportunities for reusing and recycling materials in the refurbishment. These materials may have arisen as waste on site or may originate off site	4.5.2.1
Ask the building owner and/or manager for detailed information on the location of asbestos in the building, and get advice on what action to take if asbestos is found	4.5.3.8
Any wastes arising from the works should be handled appropriately and disposed of in accordance with the legislation	4.5.3.8
Noise and vibration from works affecting the building's inhabitants	4.4.3.4 4.4.3.7
Use debris netting when carrying out external refurbishment, eg cladding, to reduce dust and protect against falling objects	4.4.1.4
Undertake surveys to identify whether protected species are present, eg bats or birds	4.1.4

Repairs to exposed structural elements (eg bridge soffits, cladding)

Key issues	Section
Prevent debris from works falling onto the ground or water below. This should be incorporated into the working methods. It is especially important for works over public areas or near watercourses and sensitive ecological sites	4.7.8
Store hazardous materials carefully to minimise the risk of spillage	4.5.2.6
Noise from the works can affect neighbours	3.3.1 4.4.3.4
Carrying out repairs over a watercourse has potential to pollute it	4.7.8
Undertake surveys to identify whether protected species are present, eg bats or birds	4.1.4

Roadworks

Key issues	Section
Minimise the risk of spillage in using oils, bitumen and chemicals	3.4
Noise and vibration may annoy neighbours. Night time working may cause additional annoyance. Ensure appropriate mitigation and monitoring are in place, and that consultation with neighbours around these activities is continued throughout the project	3.3.1 4.4.3.4 4.4.3.7
Ensure dust management techniques are used when removing upper layers of road surface and planing	4.4.1.3 4.4.1.4
Traffic entering and leaving the site may disrupt normal traffic flow. Emissions from traffic may annoy neighbours so ensure that all vehicles follow the requirements of the projects traffic management plan (TMP)	4.4.1.5 4.6.2
Recycle waste material arising from roadworks	4.5.2.1
Do not discharge gully pot residues to surface water or groundwater. Identify alternative disposal options including discharge to the foul sewer (with the consent of the local sewerage provider) after solids settlement, or to a suitably licensed waste disposal site	4.7.6

Superstructure

Key issues	Section
Installation of large structures may require night time working or road closures, ensure appropriate consents are obtained and notifications are made	4.4.3.5 4.6.2
Off-site pre-fabrication to minimise on-site impacts	4.5.2.3

Tunnelling

Key issues	Section
Ensuring that potential impacts on groundwater, which could further impact on ecological habitats or groundwater drinking supplies, have been identified and that procedures are followed to minimise the effect of the works	4.1.4 4.7.8
Determining whether abstraction license/permit and/or discharge consent/permit are required when deciding on most appropriate disposal option.	4.7.6
Ensuring that disposal of excess water is done so in a controlled manner	4.7.6
Disposal of spoil and slurry arising from tunnelling works and traffic associated with long distance transport should be undertaken in accordance with the legislation	4.6.2
Identifying buildings (especially listed buildings) sensitive to ground-borne vibration, ie in the locality of planned ground level tunnels and of tunnel portal before works begin	4.4.3.7
Consider the potential impact of nuisance, eg noise, dust or vibration, caused by 24-hour working near tunnel portals	3.3.1 4.4.3.4
Encountering contaminated ground or groundwater during tunnelling. Follow these steps if encountered: • stop work immediately • report the discovery to the site manager who should consult a specialist for advice • seal off the area to contain spread of contaminants • clear site to ensure there is nothing that could cause fire or explosion • contact the regulator or local authority once it is confirmed that contamination is found • ensure that the suspected contamination is tested and characterised and agree changes to the existing remedial plan • follow good practice guidance to remediate the land.	4.3.4
Ensuring that procedures are followed to manage the discovery of archaeological finds (including old cemeteries)	4.2.5

2.3   POST CONSTRUCTION PHASE

Demobilisation

Key issues	Section
Boreholes should be decommissioned effectively to avoid leaving pathways for pollutants	4.3.4
Demobilisation will lead to a number of waste streams especially hazardous waste through closure of Control of Substances Hazardous to Health (COSHH) storage areas. Ensure appropriate disposal	4.5.3.8
Close-out of redundant, or handover of ongoing permits and consents, eg drainage consents, abstraction licence and an Integrated Pollution Control (IPC) permit	3.2
Ensure necessary contracts are in place to fulfil any ongoing monitoring requirements, eg ecological	3.2 4.1.4

Permitting

Key issues	Section
Surrender/transfer environmental permits, ie environmental permits obtained for an on-site borehole, water from which was used for dust suppression	3.2 4.7.6
Transfer environmental permits for elements of the permanent works as required	3.2 4.7.6
Application to surrender environmental permits for use of waste material on site	3.2 4.5.3.8

Review activities (lessons learnt and good practice)

Key issues	Section
Complete final assessment of RMP or SWMP, including assessment of cost savings and identification of good practice	4.5.3.5
Write up case studies/results of trials undertaken or new technologies used and promote within company/to industry	3.2

Site handover and commissioning

Key issues	Section
Provide all necessary documentation, eg handover manuals, completed and issued	3.2
Ensure calibration of monitoring equipment before handover	3.2
Ensure maintenance requirements for critical equipment/plant are detailed and handed over	3.2
Ensure handover of any ongoing permits, licences and consents (PLCs)	3.2
If required provide training in use of IT systems/equipment/plant etc for operating team	3.2

2.4 OTHER ISSUES REQUIRING CONSIDERATION

Use of hand-held tools

Key issues	Section
Develop a refuelling protocol for the site and follow it	4.5.2.7
Maintain plant regularly to optimise fuel efficiency and prevent pollution incidents	3.2 4.4.1.5

Key issues	Section
Prevent water pollution and ground contamination. Use drip trays under stationary plant to contain oil leaks	3.4
Ensure that only trained staff use plant and that they use it for its intended purpose	3.4
Remember that water containing oils or other chemical contamination cannot be discharged to watercourses or onto the ground	4.7.6
Secure plant from vandals, as they could cause pollution incidents	3.3.3
Noise and vibration from plant, eg generators and poker vibrators, may annoy neighbours and disturb ecology. Where possible, use quiet plant and apply noise abatement techniques	4.4.3.4 4.4.3.7

Use of plant and equipment

Key issues	Section
Designate an area within the site compound for routine plant maintenance. Plant maintenance area should be on hard-standing and remote from surface water drains	3.2
Surface water runoff from plant maintenance may contain pollutants, eg oils. Prevent their release especially to controlled waters	4.7.3
Ensure that appropriately trained staff carry out repairs to plant	3.2
Develop a protocol for disposing of wastes from maintenance	4.5.3.6
Dispose of old filters carefully as they contain substantial quantities of oil. All engine oils/waste oils (except edible oils) are hazardous/special waste	4.5.3.10
Encourage the use of biodegradable oil substitutes over non-biodegradable where appropriate	4.5.2.3
Recycle used oils	4.5.2.1
Tyres cannot be sent to landfill, so find an appropriate route for recycling them	4.5.2.1
Prepare for spillages. Display the site's emergency response procedure at the plant maintenance area. Ensure a spill kit is kept there and that all site staff know how to use it. Carry a spill kit in all repair vehicles	3.4
Check replacement periods for hydraulic pipework and carry out regular checks. Use biodegradable oil for hydraulics where appropriate. Blowouts regularly cause pollution incidents	3.4

Use of oils and chemicals

Key issues	Section
COSHH assessments need to be held on site for any potentially hazardous materials. These provide advice on the type of storage needed for the chemicals, ie bunded areas, storage of flammable products in locked cupboards	4.5.2.6
Well managed and maintained storage of hazardous materials reduces waste and the risk of spillages, which could result in possible ground or groundwater contamination. Store all potentially polluting substances away from surface and foul water drains, watercourses and sensitive areas	4.5.2.6
Oil storage must be in accordance with the legislation and prevent contamination of the water environment	4.5.2.6
Transfer chemicals between containers only within a suitably bunded area. Spillages outside this area could result in ground or water contamination	4.7.3
When using fuel, follow the refuelling protocol to minimise the risk of spillage	4.5.2.7
Minimise accidental spillages and have emergency procedures in place in case of a spill. Make spill kits available and ensure site staff are trained to use them	3.4
Any disposal of product or empty product containers should be in accordance with waste management legislation and the related COSHH datasheet	4.5.2.6
Provide security measures for the site and storage areas to prevent vandalism and theft. Storage system valves, taps, hatches or lids and delivery hoses should be fitted with locks and locked when not in use. Where possible materials should be stored in secure containers or buildings	3.3.3 4.5.2.6

Working near water

Key issues	Section
Check that permission has been obtained for any temporary works	4.7.8
Special consideration needs to be taken when working on pontoons and barges to ensure risk of water pollution is minimised	4.7.8
Supervise closely all plant refuelling. Fill portable fuel tanks and spare fuel containers away from the water's edge and never overfill	4.5.2.7
Keep adequate supplies of booms and oil absorbent material available at all times for emergency use in case of a spillage. Dispose of any used absorbents in accordance with legislation	3.4 4.5.3.8
Prevent pollution from plant used near a watercourse. Maintain plant regularly. Use drip trays	4.7.8
Ensure runoff from haul roads near or over watercourses cannot enter the watercourse	4.7.8
Erect temporary haul road bridges to prevent pollution and damage to stream beds	4.7.3
Where watercourse embankments are stripped of vegetation, stabilise them to prevent erosion. This may be done by seeding them using clover or fast growing grasses and covering with biodegradable sheeting	4.7.8

Key issues	Section
Prevent dust or litter blowing into watercourses	4.4.1.4 4.7.8
Be aware of potential direct or indirect disturbance to the bankside and in-stream ecology	4.1.4
Ensure works are secured from vandals	3.3.3

Working with groundwater

Key issues	Section
Notify the environmental regulator where extensive dewatering is to occur so they may issue the relevant licence/permit	4.7.6
Any groundwater abstracted from site needs to be disposed of. Generally the best environmental option is to return it to groundwater. Contact the environmental regulator for advice before adopting this solution as a discharge consent may be required	4.7.6
There is a risk of mobilising ground contamination when working with groundwater and a potential risk of ground instability. If any contamination is suspected, consult a specialist for advice before proceeding and if any is encountered during the works	4.3.4
Undertake appropriate site investigations to assess groundwater contamination and monitor for petrol/oil or diesel compounds that may float or are dissolved before carrying out any further work. Liaise with regulator on course of action	3.2.4 4.7.8
Works affecting groundwater may have an effect on nearby ecology. Consult an ecologist before any works are carried out and agree a method statement (MS) with the environmental regulator	4.1.4
Dewatering may cause a change in groundwater levels and affect river/stream flows. A solution is to monitor water levels in sensitive areas and recharge with the extracted groundwater of the correct quality and temperature	4.7.6
Minimise the risk of spillage when using oils and chemicals	3.4

3   General project management

3.1   THE MANAGEMENT FRAMEWORK

This section outlines an approach for managing the environment on site. Steps 1 to 5 should be followed for every site.

3.1.1   Five steps to successful project management

Team work is essential to deliver effective environmental management on site. This includes inputs from the main contractor and subcontractors (on site), the contractors' organisation (off site), environmental manager/representative/clerk of works, designers, clients, customer and suppliers. To manage this teamwork effectively the site manager (and the managers of subcontractors) should follow these steps:

Step 1 Identify the environmental obligations of the project

- Review any environmental assessments (eg EIA), associated reports (eg ES) and surveys that have been carried out (eg for protected species or contaminated land) and any other client/designer serviced assessment.

- Identify legal and other obligations (including requirements to adopt assessment schemes such as CEEQUAL and BREEAM) (see **Section 1.4**).

- Identify environmental requirements (eg PLCS) contained in the project brief, specification or contract documents (eg KPIs).

- Consult with the relevant regulator(s) – be proactive to give the regulator an opportunity to identify and address issues at an early planning stage.

- Consult with other relevant interested parties as required, including local residents.

Step 2 Identify the environmental aspects and impacts (risks) associated with the activities (including potential emergencies) particular to the site

- Review relevant documentation identified in Step 1.

- Compile an environmental aspects and impacts (risk) register for the site (see **Case study 3.1**) that links on-site activities with sensitive receptors (eg neighbours or ecology) and communicate these to site-based staff during inductions.

- Talk to environmental regulators and other stakeholders, such as local authorities, about their concerns for the site at an early stage.

- Discuss and agree potential pollution incident management procedure(s) for identified environmental aspects.

- Liaise with clients and designers to establish how they can help identify and overcome potential environmental difficulties.

Step 3 Identify environmental responsibilities

- Define the environmental responsibilities of all site-based staff, including those who are involved in implementing and monitoring initiatives.
- Define lines of communication between site-based staff, and those responsible for producing the site environmental plan.
- Ensure all site staff with environmental responsibilities have the required resources, training and competence to fulfil the role.

Step 4 Establishing appropriate plans to manage site activities

- Information gathered in Steps 1 to 3 can be used to form the basis of necessary plans needed to manage the activities of the project.
- These plans include an overarching EMP that is site-specific, accessible, regularly reviewed (and updated when necessary) and always in use.
- Use the EMP to develop risk assessments and MS for specific aspects of site activities.
- MS are important documents on site as these will be referenced during the project and will incorporate not only environmental, but also all other requirements, eg health and safety and buildability. For example, if work is in an area of environmental importance/ significance or in, near to or liable to affect water the regulator should be consulted before the start of any works to agree the MS. This may form part of the planning conditions.
- Other plans developed to support management of site activities are emergency plans, plans incorporating project assessment scheme requirements (see Section 1.4), RMP or a SWMP.
- Section 1.3 outlines how the EMP can fit into the EMS of the company.

Step 5 Monitoring

- A robust monitoring system should be implemented to demonstrate the requirements of the EMP are met, eg weekly site environmental checklists, highlighting any issues, and describing actions taken.
- All monitoring data should be retained, so there is an auditable trail. Monitoring refers to a wide range of activities, including:
    - waste data
    - energy and fuel use
    - audit reports
    - maintaining and reviewing training records
    - chemical analysis of discharges and/or baseline levels and nearby streams

- ○ waste transfer evidence or consignment notes
- ○ records of dust generation
- ○ noise monitoring records
- ○ licence conditions.
- Measures should be in place to rectify any non-compliance with the EMP that is raised during monitoring.

> Communicate to all site-based staff during inductions that there is a duty of care on everyone to report any issues (such as spills, damage to materials, or complaints from neighbours) that are encountered during the construction-phase of a project.

- Monitoring will provide baseline data that can be used for setting objectives and targets for tracking during construction and into the operational phase (post site handover).

Aspects and impacts assessment form (courtesy Kier)

Kier has created an excel-based aspects and impacts (A&I) assessment form to be used by pre-construction and construction teams on all its projects.

It is the intention that the form is completed initially by pre-construction teams to identify which of the nine environmental aspects defined by Kier are applicable to projects:

Environmental aspects

1 Emissions to air.
2 Emissions to land.
3 Emissions to water.
4 Waste generation.
5 Nuisance and environmental health.
6 Ecology and biodiversity.
7 Cultural heritage.
8 Use of raw materials.
9 Use of natural resource.

For those aspects identified as relevant to a project, an assessment of the following steps is followed:

- likely impact (eg for example spill of fuel/COSHH substances to land causing pollution)
- whether the occurrence of the aspect is normal/abnormal or emergency
- initial impact (likelihood and consequence)
- local control(s) to manage the impact, for example locate fuel storage on hard-standing if possible. Ensure substances are stored in accordance with COSHH assessments
- residual impact as result of the control local(s) being applied (likelihood and consequence).

To determine both the initial and residual impact consideration needs to be given the associated risk(s).

To make this determination, the user should refer to the impacts matrix (Figure 3.1) to decide on the combined likelihood (ranging from unlikely to definite) and consequence (ranging from no harm to immediate long-term catastrophic harm) of the aspect. This will determine the local control(s) required to reduce/eliminate the risk and determine the residual impact.

			Intolerable – Tolerable – Acceptable					
Immediate long-term catastrophic harm	F	F1	F2	F3	F4	F5	F6
Immediate long-term harm	E	E1	E2	E3	E4	E5	E6
Limited short-term harm	D	D1	D2	D3	D4	D5	D6
Minor harm	C	C1	C2	C3	C4	C5	C6
Minimal harm	B	B1	B2	B3	B4	B5	B6
No harm	A	A1	A2	A3	A4	A5	A6
		1	2	3	4	5	6
		Improbable (unlikely)	Remote (doubtful)	Rare (occasional)	Probably (likely)	Frequent (regular)	Certain (definite)

(Consequence — vertical axis label; Likelihood — horizontal axis label)

Potential environmental benefit	A+	Return to EAP		View user guide
Environmental benefit	A++			

Figure 3.1   Impact matrix

The A&I form is a tool to identify and minimise negative impacts arising from aspects. In addition, the form includes consideration of environmental benefits by identifying these aspects and defining local control(s) that provide opportunity to create new benefits and/or maintain those already established (eg protected species habitats).

Resulting from consideration of the initial impact (positive or negative), the risk associated with it, local controls and residual impact (positive or negative) an environmental action plan (EAP) is defined for a project.

The completed A&I form then feeds into a projects EMP and is passed to construction teams for ongoing management and review.

The principle contractor needs to demonstrate that the environmental responsibilities of subcontractors or others working on behalf of the organisation, such as suppliers and/or consultants, are clearly defined and communicated.

It is important that any queries are resolved and recorded at an early stage to avoid misunderstandings and problems during construction.

The better responsibilities are defined and understood the more likely they are to be adopted.

3.1.2   Working with regulators

Whatever the size of the project it will be necessary to work with regulators. Early interaction with them is important for a successful relationship. Regulators have a diverse range of specific responsibilities and powers to enforce legislation. Some of their main responsibilities are included in **Table 3.1**.

Table 3.1 *Regulatory categories and their core responsibilities*

Regulator	Responsibilities
Local authority	Nuisances, air quality, traffic, the planning process, environmental permits, land contamination, and flooding when acting as lead local flood authorities (LLFA)
Environmental regulator	Discharges to land, air and water, waste, water abstraction, ground and water contamination, water and land quality, engineering activities in or near waters, nature conservation and built heritage, and environmental permits/licences
Nature conservation organisations	Designated ecological sites, geological and geomorphological sites and protected species and habitats
Heritage bodies	Designated archaeological and heritage sites (including listed buildings)
County archaeologist	Designated archaeological and heritage sites
Health and Safety Executive (HSE)	Health and safety including vibration (ie from hand-held tools) and asbestos
Water and sewerage provider	Effluent discharge to public sewer (also combined drains and surface water drains), and supply of water

Full contact details for and responsibilities of key national regulators and heritage bodies are given in **Appendix A1**.

Environmental regulators should be contacted as early in the project as possible. This can help to identify the required PLCs, to agree project requirements, and to minimise project delays.

It is important to understand and manage any planning conditions and associated guidance developed from the granting of planning permission or the equivalent requirements associated with other consents granted. This should be done by involving the planning authorities from the design phase through to completion.

Projects that do not have planning conditions and non-permitted activities will also need to consider environmental aspects and impacts. So, regardless of conditions, permit requirements etc it is important to develop a constructive dialogue with regulators to ensure they are aware of what is happening on the project and why.

Dealing with regulators
Plan ahead and give regulators advance warning of potential problems
• give regulators the time they need to process the enquiry, particularly when applying for PLCs – the application processes can take many months
• always display the relevant emergency numbers (see Appendix A1 for contact details)
• ensure site-based staff know the correct procedures for reporting incidents
• always notify the relevant environmental regulator of any pollution incidents or other environmental damage (see Appendix A1)

3.1.3 Environmental responsibilities

Environmental good practice on site should start with a commitment from company executives. Everyone on site is responsible for ensuring that their actions constitute good practice. Certain individuals have clearly defined roles and responsibilities as detailed in Table 3.2, which is not an exhaustive list and it is likely that levels of responsibilities will vary within companies.

Table 3.2   Roles and responsibilities

Individual	Role
All site-based staff	• should follow good practice and are responsible for carrying out their activities without detrimental effects on the environment • should comply with systems of work including the EMP, MS and risk assessments and should carry out tasks in accordance with their training • are responsible for reporting any environmental concerns and incidents to their supervisors, including suggestions for improvements.
Site engineers/ foremen	• should understand the project environmental obligations and the practical measures needed to comply with them • should ensure that the control measures identified (EMP, MS etc) are effectively carried out • identify the need for and deliver regular toolbox talks.

Site manager	• principal responsibility for environmental management on site by ensuring:
	  o all measures in the EMP, including consents, are obtained and implemented on site. This includes ensuring that adequate resources are allocated to environmental management on site
	  o environmental issues in MS/risk assessments are effectively communicated on site and that appropriate training (including induction) is delivered
	  o regular environmental inspections are carried out
	  o environmental instructions from the client are carried out
	  o incidents and non-conformances are investigated, corrected and prevented from reoccurring
	• liaise with all appropriate stakeholders, including regulators as required.

Environmental co-ordinator/ advisor	• carry out environmental duties including:
	  o producing documentation
	  o liaison with third parties
	  o inspections and audits
	  o delivering environmental training and toolbox talks
	  o investigation of incidents and non-conformances are corrected and preventative action implemented
	  o reporting environmental performance to senior management
	  o providing help and advice to the site managers/site engineers/foremen
	  o reviewing and inputting into risk assessments and MS.

Individual	Role
Designer	• ensures that environmental aspects are considered and incorporated into the design as appropriate, and that all residual issues or impacts are communicated to the client/principal contractor • ensures environmental aspects are identified and mitigated.
Manager (site or main office based)	• provide corporate advice on environmental legislation, good practice and company environmental policy, and translate decisions into action at site level • review training needs and arrange for it to be provided.
Director with responsibility for the environment/ executive board	• responsible for: ○ overall environmental governance and strategy ○ company legislative compliance ○ ensuring an environmental policy is developed ○ ensuring that environmental aspects are identified and controlled for all projects ○ ensure adequate resources are allocated to achieve the environmental standards set out by the company.
Client	• ensures that all relevant environmental documentation and information, eg existing consents, is communicated to the designer and contractor • setting the standard for environmental management on site, as stated in the contracts • reporting any environmental concerns and responding appropriately to incidents.

3.1.4   The supply chain

The supply chain needs to understand their environmental obligations and contract requirements, and demonstrate how they intend to fulfil them. As with any controls, environmental responsibility can be implemented through incentives and/or penalties. It is important for contractors and subcontractors to work together to ensure

> Successful environmental management relies on communication. It is crucial that everyone is aware of the key issues, has the relevant information to deal with them, understands their responsibilities and provides feedback to those in charge.

successful delivery of projects. The following checklist provides suggestions on selecting and managing subcontractors:

Selecting and managing subcontractors	✓

Subcontractors should be assessed on the basis of their environmental performance such as:
 	
• proof of their past environmental performance along with records of past and pending prosecutions
• quality of MS and risk assessments
• competence of their staff including, but not limited to:
   ○ Construction Skills Certification Scheme (CSCS)
   ○ Site Environmental Awareness Training Scheme (SEATS)
   ○ City and Guilds
   ○ National Vocational Qualifications (NVQs)
   ○ Chartered specialists
• contractor membership schemes, for example the Supply Chain Sustainability School
• quality of their management systems for the environment, for example ISO 14001 certification	

Ensure that subcontractors sign up to the implementation of the EMP and other site specific plans such as the RMP/SWMP before starting work	
Ensure subcontractors attend environmental training sessions/inductions (eg using toolbox talks)	
Ensure subcontractors are aware of their environmental obligations on the project	
The contract should include requirements to follow good environmental practice	
Audit the performance of subcontractors during the project	
Agree a corrective action process with the principal contractor to record and monitor improvement actions that are closed out	

3.1.5 Raising awareness

It is important to raise awareness of environmental issues so that people on site know what environmental good practice is and know where to obtain information. Many contractors, particularly on large projects, employ both an environmental advisor/consultant who are able to collaborate with regulators and site-based staff/managers to demonstrate that good practice is pursued throughout the duration of construction.

CIRIA: www.ciria.org/training

CITB SEATS: http://tinyurl.com/kzmlnuw

City and Guilds: www.cityandguilds.com

CSCS: www.cscs.uk.com

Supply Chain Sustainability School: www.supplychainschool.co.uk

Training should be provided on site to disseminate good practice guidance relevant to a particular project. For a training programme to be successful, it is vital to:

- select a trainer with appropriate knowledge, skills and experience (often peer-level training is most effective)
- make training specific to the audience
- posting key environmental issues relating to the programme stages on to notice boards (as shown in **Figure 3.2**) in communal areas can keep awareness raised to all workforce
- make training engaging and relevant
- follow up and refresh training to keep abreast of changes in legislation and codes of practice
- use refresher training and inductions as a response to corrective actions raised (eg misuse of spill kits, incorrect refuelling methods)
- check the understanding of the training with the attendees through tests, discussions, inspections, audits etc
- maintain records of all training undertaken/planned.

Key aspects of training for site managers and engineers should include:

- pollution prevention
- resource management (materials, water, energy and waste)
- ecology and archaeology awareness
- emergency procedures for environmental incidents
- choice of plant, plant maintenance and safe refuelling
- PLCs management and monitoring requirements
- choice of working methods
- practical actions to demonstrate compliance with relevant legislation
- importance of good housekeeping
- importance of sustainable use of resources
- sources of advice
- personal responsibility/liability.

Figure 3.2   *Environmental information board (courtesy BAM Nuttall)*

All site-based staff should be given a site induction, which should include site-specific environmental risks and their control and management. Further training such as spill kit use should be given to all relevant site-based staff (**Figure 3.3**). For training to be effective, adequate time should be set aside to inform people about the issues that are relevant to the site and work.

3.1.6 Client and designer responsibilities

Designers should consider the environmental impact of their designs by conducting an environmental risk assessment. If the design of temporary or permanent works compromises environmental good practice, the designer should be informed.

Where the contract imposes environmental constraints it is worth discussing the reasons with the designers and/or client. It may be possible to explore alternative approaches that have less impact such as using recycled or secondary aggregate, and heating, ventilating and air conditioning (HVAC) systems or mechanical ventilation heat recovery (MVHR) systems.

Figure 3.3   Spill drill training (courtesy BAM Nuttall)

3.1.7 Environmental Management Systems (EMS)

An EMS takes a systematic approach to assessing, managing and monitoring the environmental impacts. This includes the definition of management responsibilities and development of documented procedures. The systematic approach means all staff are aware of what is expected of them and provides consistency throughout the organisation.

> Toolbox talks should be carried out on a regular basis on aspects appropriate to the construction works. Copies of those produced by BUILD UK, CECA, CIP and CIRIA are available from: **www.ciria.org/egpos**
>
> Further on-site training guidance is available from several bodies including CIRIA and environmental regulators.

The main international standard for EMS used in the UK is ISO 14001. BS 8555:2003 provides guidance on the phased implementation of an EMS to ISO 14001 and if appropriate accreditation to the Eco-Management and Audit Scheme (EMAS).

3.2 PLANNING, SETTING UP AND MANAGING THE SITE

This section outlines measures that should be considered when setting up and managing the site to achieve environmental good practice.

3.2.1   Enabling works

Liaison with the regulator

Regulators encourage contractors to take a proactive approach regarding environmental management on site, so it is important to involve them from an early stage in the project.

Site survey

Before any works begin, a survey should be carried out (if an EIA is undertaken these surveys will be included as part of the EIA process) by competent, qualified and/or experienced person(s) in-line with published good practice. It is important to survey a site early in the construction process to allow enough lead in time to avoid or mitigate any potential effects.

It is useful to contact the appropriate regulator at this stage as they can provide advice on potential sensitive areas and, if necessary, on possible mitigation options.

Surveys are divided into three phases:

1   **Desk-based indicative survey:** review drawings/plans and contract information, supported by environmental risk registers and the company's EMS. If the company does not operate an EMS or have environmental aspects and impacts (risk) registers, this stage should still be completed.

    The desk-based survey is a process of identifying where activities may have a positive or negative impact on the environment on and around the site and is based on drawings/ plans and contract information or online databases, for example MAGIC ecology. Any feature, habitat, area or living organism that can potentially be negatively affected can be termed an environmental receptor.

    Details of all receptors identified should be recorded and be cross referenced against site activities that are likely to affect them, for example scrubland would be affected by clearance/set-up removing vegetation across the site. This will form the basis of site specific environmental aspects and impacts (risk) assessment.

2   **Site walkover:** carried out by the environmental manager/advisor along with site team representatives (eg project manager, construction manager or site supervisor). This is to follow up the items recorded from the desk-based survey, reviews of drawings and site maps and those identified in contract requirements etc. On-site reviews will help to define appropriate action to control potential impacts on receptors. Also, the walkover will help decide where further assistance and/or technical surveys are needed. Also other receptors not previously identified, such as trees with nesting birds or potential bat roosts, drains not marked on site plans, invasive species or potentially contaminated ground, may be discovered.

3   **Technical surveys:** a collective term for surveys that should be conducted by a suitably qualified professional, such as noise, ecology and contaminated land surveys etc. The requirement for these surveys will be dependent on the outcome of the desk-based

survey and the site walkover and also any requirements from the client and/ or other interested parties, such as regulators. The initial surveys often recommend that further detailed technical surveys should be completed.

MAGIC providing authoritative geographic information about the natural environment from across government: **www.magic.gov.uk**

These surveys should identify any environmental receptors and can propose mitigation when agreeing working measures with regulators. They can also provide an opportunity to improve the value or add to the site during the contract.

Benefits of early environmental management planning (courtesy Galliford Try plc)

3.2

A flood defence scheme located in a densely populated area between two residential tower blocks, and next to a sensitive watercourse and reed bed containing protected species. The work involved piling, brick work, excavation and fill operations, and transporting materials. The scheme benefited from early involvement of company environmental specialists, as follows:

- nuisance (eg noise, vibration), contaminated land and ecology were identified as key issues on the environmental constraints plan, which was produced and communicated before the work on site

- a Section 61 consent was submitted and accepted by the council detailing the companies' construction activities and proposed methods of mitigation

- a letter drop produced by the site team was handed out to all residents. Communication was maintained through local residents groups to indicate when changes were expected such as asking for parked cars to be temporarily moved from the access road while the piles were delivered to site

- the sensitive ecology resulted in barriers being erected to prevent material from works falling into these areas

- land contamination was identified as a potential risk and communicated to the site team through toolbox talks. When contamination was found, containment was put in place to ensure no risk to operatives and members of the public. Waste was recycled instead of going to landfill where practicable. The framework environmental advisor was kept involved in this process from early identification, through to contaminant and removal from site

- because of early and continued involvement, no complaints were received from the residents regarding the work. Also, no environmental incident resulted from the activities. The Environment Agency as the client was impressed with the environmental standards achieved, and special praise was received from the noise team at the local council who were delighted with the excellent standard of work.

Site clearance

It is important to plan the site clearance at the appropriate time of year, in order to comply with legislation and to avoid disruption to wildlife such as during the breeding season, which is one aspect identified requiring consideration for a number of species within **Figure 4.1**.

Weekly meetings

These can be a highly effective way of managing risk and change. Potential conflicts can be identified early and allow all parties to work together to develop solutions. A

---

proactive approach can introduce alternative working methods, additional resources and equipment, and extended working hours (including weekend and night shifts) to alleviate programme pressures.

The meeting should be fully minuted for the benefit of all parties to assist with later negotiations and contract resolutions should they arise.

3.2.2 Site offices

When planning the site layout, contractors' offices incorporating welfare facilities and equipment should be sited to minimise pollution and other forms of disturbance to surrounding neighbours. Also, site offices need to be located, so as not to cause any environmental impact (eg destruction of ecological habitats). Hedges or existing trees can be used to screen sites and compounds in rural areas. In urban areas the construction works are usually screened with suitable hoarding or acoustic screens.

Consideration should also be made with regards to the avoidance of greenfield sites (where practicable), and potential flood zones, as well as transport links to site when considering travel planning for deliveries and the workforce.

There are many general environmental issues relating to the internal office environment including energy use, waste (eg paper use, toner cartridge) and the use of electrical equipment to consider.

Carbon management and energy efficiency are important considerations for the entire construction process and HM Government (2013) contains a strategic priority on 'low carbon and sustainable construction'. Site offices have been identified as important contributors to carbon emissions from the construction process and should be assessed on their energy performance.

3.2.3 Site management

Most pollution incidents, environmental damage or other causes of complaints can be avoided through careful planning, training and communication of issues on site. Most measures needed to prevent pollution are inexpensive, especially if they are included at the planning stage. In contrast, the costs of cleaning up a pollution incident or repairing environmental damage can be very high, as can abatement measures put in place as a response to complaints.

Pollution prevention and waste minimisation measures may offer substantial economic benefits. These include reducing the need for expensive raw materials, fewer site accidents and a reduced risk of prosecution for environmental offences. Introduction of pollution prevention measures is the first step, but for these to be effective, managers should be committed and staff should understand why they are needed and be suitably trained.

The following checklist details steps to be taken in managing a site, but is not exhaustive as some sites will have their own unique issues that need to be appropriately managed.

Site management	✓
Define environmental responsibilities	
Identify the site specific environmental aspects and impacts (risks) and implement controls	
Establish contact with appropriate regulators and relevant interested parties, such as stakeholders	
Ensure everyone on site is aware of their responsibilities/roles and liabilities	
Through a site induction, make everyone aware of the project environmental issues and environmental standards	
Site-based staff need to be aware of environmental emergency procedures (damage to/or injury to protected species, silt runoff, fire etc)	
Engage and inform any neighbours of works to be undertaken	
Adequately protect site against vandalism, theft and breakage	
Ensure all consents/licences/permits have been obtained before any activities controlled by them is carried out (eg water discharge from site)	
A drainage plan identifying foul and surface water drainage needs to be accessible	
Mark drains appropriately to distinguish them	
Identify nearby rivers, streams or groundwater etc and ensure they are protected where necessary and inspected regularly	
Identify restricted areas for archaeology, ecology, soil storage and protect	
Provide bunds and/or internally bunded tanks for polluting substances such as fuel/oil/chemicals/paints etc	
Provide a waste storage area – to include clear segregation of waste types such as hazardous, non-hazardous (including recyclables) and inert waste taking into consideration site compound size	
Designate concrete washout area	
Provide wheel wash or road cleaning equipment	
Indicate all designated haul routes	
Display environmental awareness posters/bulletins	
Display warning signs on site prominently	
Have company environmental policy readily available for reference	
Establish, implement and monitor effectiveness of control measures for potential nuisance (eg noise, dust, odours or vibration)	
Consider adopting accredited schemes to aid project environmental management such as CCS, CEEQUAL, BREEM (see Section 1.4)	

Environmental good practice on site guide, fourth edition

3.2.4 Environmental aspects and impacts and risk assessment

The identification of environmental A&Is and carrying out a risk assessment helps to decide whether those identified are significant. Decisions are then made on the need for and scope of control and mitigation measures.

The approach to risk assessment is usually staged to allow an understanding of risks to build to a point where environmental impacts can be adequately characterised and understood.

Risk assessors gather all the relevant information regarding the site, developing an understanding of its history, environmental setting and the construction activities. This in turn informs subsequent decisions that may need to be made about the site. Usually, each stage in the risk assessment process involves gathering data of increasing complexity and analysis.

Risk assessment can be a highly technical exercise of increasing complexity (especially where contaminated land, archaeology, heritage and ecological features are concerned) to demonstrate whether there are unacceptable (significant) risks that have to be managed. Technical experts such as archaeologists, contaminated land experts and ecologists may be required to assist the project team where these risks are apparent.

There are a number of models that can be used to aid with the identification of environmental aspects and impacts. The source, pathway (including new ones that may be created by the construction project) and receptor model is a widely accepted concept in environmental risk assessment, in each environmental impact link, an assessment can be made of the significance and degree of risk (**Figure 3.4**).

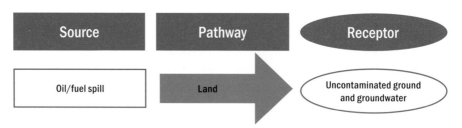

Figure 3.4   Source-pathway-receptor model

Risk assessment is the likelihood and consequences of events that affect the environment, which most commonly involves a mixture of qualitative and quantitative risk assessment methodology.

EMS systems certified to ISO 14001 require significant aspects and impacts and those operational control measures to avoid the negative effects(s) to be identified through an environmental risk assessment.

Organisations usually undertake risk assessments and present the results in the form of a project-specific A&I register or risk register as part of the company EMS with the identified control measures incorporated into the project EMP.

In some instances there is a legal requirement to undertake environmental risk assessment. This can be, for example, when required as a planning condition due to the presence of contaminated land, archaeology, heritage or ecology (**Figure 3.5**) or under the Town and Country Planning (EIA) Regulations 2011 where certain projects are identified as requiring a full ES to be submitted for consultation as part of the planning process.

**Figure 3.5   Ancient woodland signage
(courtesy Skanska)**

Planning approval grants permission for the project in accordance with the ES, which will identify significant aspects and impacts before, during and after construction and controls, mitigation and monitoring measures to be incorporated. Projects must then incorporate these requirements into the EMP following the approved ES and/or discharge of planning conditions agreed control, mitigation and monitoring measures. These must then be followed on site.

Whether risk assessment is legally required or not on the project, it is always recommended that an environmental risk assessment is completed. This is to ensure risks are adequately identified and managed, and to ensure the environment, the project progress and the company are not adversely affected as a result of any potential breach, eg pollution incident.

3.2.5   Procuring and managing materials (and plant)

Considering the environmental impact during the procurement of materials has many benefits for the site (see **Section 4.5.2.3**). It is advisable to establish a procurement strategy that can be applied on each site. Such a strategy should consider:

- substituting virgin materials for those with recycled content
- substituting hazardous materials for non-hazardous alternatives (less pollution potential, safer to use for employees, easier and cheaper to dispose)
- ethically and/or sustainably sourced materials and products, eg the Forest Stewardship Council (FSC) and the Programme for the Endorsement of Forest Certification (PEFC) certified timber, BES 6001, ETI and GRI

- consider locally sourced goods

- the embodied energy, CO_2 and water of materials when selecting products (as part of assessing the whole-life impact of the project)

- energy use of equipment and facilities such as site offices

- water consumption of equipment and facilities, ie recycling vehicle wash waters, rainwater capture, low flush, waterless urinals, spray taps, efficiency attachments

- consider just-in-time (JIT) delivery options to avoid damage at the site due to lack of storage capacity, avoid bulk ordering consider standard material sizes, pod or prefabricated materials/structures to avoid site waste and material damage on site

- consider the procurement of reusable materials, ie shuttering, hoarding fencing

- use competent suppliers and contractors to reduce environmental risks, ie those with accreditations such as CHAS, recognised management systems such as ISO 14001, no incidents or prosecutions, good references, and continued good service.

Making changes to procurement to incorporate such suggestions may not be a simple task, so developing a strategy that can be applied on more than one project will allow continued improvement. Selection of materials is critical and forms a significant part of environmental and sustainability assessment schemes on projects (see **Section 1.4**).

Managing materials

Improving the management of materials and components has environmental benefits through increased resource and site efficiency. Where site-based staff follow established procedures for managing materials and components (see **Section 4.5.2.6**) there will be fewer incidents of spillages and contamination arising from incorrect storage or handling, and less damage to materials and components. This means less waste of raw materials (see **Section 4.5.2.1**). The introduction of a RMP or SWMP means that site-based staff should be aware of and plan for the management, storage and disposal of materials that come on site in advance. This requires well planned ordering and management of materials. Also, good housekeeping on site will ensure good storage and less waste.

Ordering and receiving deliveries	
Develop a procurement strategy that considers the environmental life cycle of materials	
Reduce use of hazardous materials	
Use more materials with recycled content	
Order the correct quantity of materials to arrive when they are needed to reduce the required storage time and risk of damage and theft	
Find out in what form materials will be delivered, so that the appropriate unloading plant can be arranged and space set aside	

Ordering and receiving deliveries	✓
Ensure deliveries are received by a member of site-based staff who is able to carry out a quality inspection to avoid wastage	
Select packaging materials for deliveries that can assist effective/secure storage and movement of materials on site. Discuss opportunities for packaging 'take back' schemes with suppliers	
Arrange take back schemes for excess materials	
Avoid sensitive times for deliveries, eg rush hour, school run	

Storage

It is important to manage storage areas on site efficiently (Figure 3.6) to reduce the risk of environmental damage (eg water pollution), injury to site-based staff and theft. When storing materials keep the following points in mind:

- ensure that the suppliers' instructions are being followed

- plan the storage area so that frequently used items are easy to access

- store valuable materials, or those that are hazardous or attractive to thieves, in a secure area, out of sight of the public

- store materials away from waste storage containers and from vehicle movements that could cause accidental damage

- secure lightweight materials to protect them from wind damage or loss

- take special care over the storage of materials that are potentially polluting (see Section 4.5.2.6)

- storage and use of perishable items (eg bags of cement) should follow the 'first in first out' rule

- store on impermeable, level areas to avoid damage

- store materials away from heavy traffic to avoid impact and damage

- storage materials away from watercourses and drains to avoid pollution from spillages

- protect storage areas from the elements to minimise risk of pollution (ie silty runoff).

Figure 3.6   Good housekeeping (courtesy Laing O'Rourke)

Handling

Handling of materials on site should be kept to a minimum to avoid the risk of damage and/or injury to site-based staff. Materials should be handled using only the appropriate apparatus including cranes, trucks, fork lifts and manual handling. Ensure that the suppliers' instructions on their operation are always followed.

Reuse of materials on site

Be aware of the potential to reuse existing materials on site, for example:

* potentially valuable construction products that could be salvaged from existing buildings

* using excavated soils (this may be subject to an environmental permitting exemption or CL:AIRE (2011) code of practice and other materials, on other areas of the site (eg for raising ground level or for general landscaping)

* stockpiles of soil or other organic materials that could result in contaminated runoff into watercourses etc should be stabilised immediately by covering them with appropriate sheeting or seeding with fast growing vegetation

* pallets delivered to the site in temporary works

* left over materials of products from other areas of the site or other sites (possibly through a site warehouse) (reuse on other sites may be subject to an environmental permitting/licence exemption)

* hardcore, planning and waste concrete, eg for landscaping or footpaths (this may be subject to waste management environmental permit/licence/exemption)

* maintain good housekeeping

* 'reusable' materials such as fencing and shuttering.

3.2.6 Traffic and access routes

There are many good reasons to manage traffic coming to site, on site and departing the site. Traffic on roads in and around the site can cause nuisance through noise, exhaust emissions, dust, congestion, and create a safety hazard both on and off site. Often, common sources of complaint are the emissions, noise and visual intrusion of queuing vehicles.

Access routes

The use of public roads for site access may be restricted in terms of:

* vehicle weight and width

* time

* parking

* minimising pedestrian conflict

- low-headroom (eg low bridge)
- vehicle numbers.

Consultation with the local police and local highway authority to address these issues and effectively manage them should occur before works begin. A TMP should be devised and incorporated into the site management plan (see Section 4.6.2).

Managing site traffic

Plan the timing of deliveries to avoid vehicles waiting. Where several deliveries are likely to take place over a short period, designate a waiting area some distance from the site and call in deliveries when access is clear.

Arrange suitable designated car parking areas for site-based staff to reduce public inconvenience. Consider using a park-and-ride or car-share scheme.

Often, construction sites are blamed for disturbance caused by vehicles that are not associated with the site. To avoid this, give the main contractor and regular delivery vehicles visible identifying marks.

Managing site traffic	
Develop a traffic management plan	
Designate an area of the site for site-based staff vehicles	
Put procedures in place to prevent delivery vehicles from queuing outside the site boundary	
Make suppliers/subcontractors/delivery drivers aware of traffic restrictions on and around the site	
Inspect, service and carry out maintenance of vehicles regularly for efficient running, including subcontractors where relevant	
Delivery vehicle engines should be turned off while waiting to be unloaded	
Vehicles should be loaded and unloaded off the highway where possible	
Provide wheel washing facilities (Figure 3.7) to avoid the spread of mud onto public highways, if this is not possible arrange for a road sweeper to regularly clear the road	

3.2.7   Site demobilisation following completion

This is a phase of the works that usually receives little attention, but it can cause a number of problems. In clearing the site it is vital that wastes are managed in accordance with the legislation (see Section 4.5.3), including avoiding burning of any clearance materials. Before a project is considered to be complete, the contractor is required to clear away, and remove from the site, all equipment and materials including:

- plant
- surplus materials
- waste and skips
- rubbish and litter
- residues
- signage
- cabins
- temporary works.

Any materials removed during the site demobilisation are still subject to transport management plans, loading procedures, waste management etc. This includes unused materials stored or taken to another site.

Figure 3.7 *Wheel wash facility (courtesy Skanska)*

3.3 INTERACTION WITH THE LOCAL COMMUNITY

3.3.1 Communication and community relations

Developing effective communication and consultation with the local community is important to minimise the likelihood of causing a nuisance (eg noise, dust, waste). Such communication should be initiated, where possible at the planning stage, otherwise at the start of the project and continued throughout.

If the community is aware of what is happening, it is it is likely that complaints will be reduced. Be prepared to explain the project and to answer questions. Do not deviate from the company or client commitments, or agree additional measures. Use public meetings with the local community and stakeholders as an opportunity to listen and reassure.

Public consultation is particularly important when operations that cause disturbance are being carried out for a significant period of time. Try to explain the efforts that are being made to limit the impacts of operations by phasing activities and other control measures. When considering how to liaise with the local community, follow the steps in the checklist here:

Liaising with local community	✅
Identify and keep informed key local community representatives, such as parish councillors and residents representatives	
Visit occupants of sensitive buildings (such as schools, nursing homes and hospitals) and keep them informed of progress	
Prepare a leaflet and distribute it to nearby residents or occupiers. Provide updates or regular contributions to existing community newsletters	
Engage with the local community by working with schools, including visits and charities	
Write articles about the progress on site for the local media	
Display a 'contact board' at the site perimeter so that the public know who to contact if they have a complaint or a comment. Use this board to display information on project phasing and other relevant matters	
Join the Considerate Constructors Scheme (CCS) (see Section 1.4)	
Establish a complaint line and call it to ensure that it works	
Deal quickly with any complaints that arise and in accordance with a defined complaints procedure. Create a log of complaints. Make sure all complaints are properly followed up and resolved, and the responses to them are recorded	
Issue site-based staff with contact cards to give to the public if approached to ensure complaints/queries are dealt with effectively	
Install observatory panels in the site hoardings	

Note that some points are only appropriate to large sites

Site staff off-site

Good community relations can be quickly undone by the actions of site-based staff when off site. Ensure that all site-based staff know what is expected of them. Causes of annoyance to the community can include:

- noise on arriving or leaving site
- too many site-based staff in local shops
- offensive language and behaviour
- vehicle parking on residential streets
- leaving vehicles running
- playing loud radios
- litter dropping.

Good housekeeping

Good housekeeping is an important part of good environmental practice and it helps everyone to maintain a more efficient and safer site (**Figure 3.9**). The site should be tidy,

Engagement with the community – bug hotel (courtesy Parsons Brinckerhoff)

Issue

The extension of the Hutton Substation in Cumbria, caused some disruption to the surrounding villages in the area. Electricity Alliance North's (EAN) site staff came up with the idea of giving something back to the community by building a bug hotel at the nearby primary school using materials from the site (Figure 3.8).

Lessons learnt

The bug hotel was built by the school children and EAN representatives in Old Hutton Primary School's wildlife garden. Before going out to build the bug hotel, EAN's environmental advisor went into the classroom to talk to the pupils about the bug hotel and the type of animals and insects that might live in it.

The majority of the materials were sourced from site and included:

Figure 3.8   Bug hotel

● pallets
● bricks, stones and sand
● cardboard
● sticks and leaf litter
● plastic pipes
● bamboo and drinking straws
● terracotta plant pots.

Huw Davies, head teacher at Old Hutton Primary School, said: *"The idea of setting up a bug hotel in the school grounds has really got the children's imaginations running wild. They've all had a great day helping to build the hotel and they're excited to see what kind of guests check in over the next couple of months."*

The bug hotel provided an excellent opportunity for EAN to give something back to the community. It also provided a positive and fun learning experience for the pupils, and can continue to be used throughout the year.

EAN is made up of Parsons Brinckerhoff, Murphy and Siemens.

secure, and have clear access routes that are well signposted. The appearance of a tidy, well-managed site can reduce the likelihood of theft, vandalism or complaints.

Figure 3.9   Tidy and organised site (courtesy Mace)

Good housekeeping	✓
Adequately plan the site with designated areas of materials and waste storage	
Segregate different types of waste as it is produced and arrange frequent removal	
Keep the site tidy and clean – remember a tidy site is a safe site	
Ensure that no wind-blown litter or debris leaves the site, use covered skips to prevent wind-blown litter	
Ensure that material and plant storage areas are properly managed. Cover lightweight materials with sheeting if necessary	
Keep hoardings tidy – repair and repaint when necessary, removing any fly posting or graffiti	
Frequently brush-clean wheel washing facilities	
Keep haul routes clean	
Keep roads free from mud by using a road sweeper	
Ensure site is secure	

Working hours

Site working hours can create considerable concern and annoyance among neighbours. On some projects, working hours for noisy operations are defined by the contract documents, planning conditions or by local authorities – perhaps through a Section 61 consent (see

Section 4.4.3.4). This route should be followed early in the project to reduce the likelihood of delays and complaints being made to the local authority.

There may be opportunities for extending working hours in consultation with the local authority, but their effect on neighbours should be considered carefully – try to restrict working to sociable hours. When extended working is needed, it is important to inform neighbours in advance of the reasons for the work and its duration. Do not assume that the community's preference is for normal working hours as it may prefer longer working hours to reduce the overall length of time that they will be disrupted.

Ensure that activities are carefully timed within the working day. For example, in the same way that it is advisable to schedule deliveries outside of rush hour, other intrusive activities can be scheduled at less sensitive times. To understand the constraints, which will vary from site to site, it is important to understand the daily patterns of the neighbours. Some points to consider include:

- in city centre sites night time noise may be more acceptable than daytime noise if there are no residential areas
- avoid noisy activities during school/college/university hours (particularly during exam periods)
- local restaurants appreciate less disturbance over lunch and dinner time
- whether local businesses might require quieter periods during the day
- whether weekend or night time working is especially sensitive
- whether particularly sensitive areas (eg hospital, churches, and residential care homes) are located near the site.

3.3.2   Lighting

Lighting can be an important deterrent to vandals and thieves, but it can annoy the local residents and disturb ecology. Keep any site lighting at the minimum brightness necessary for adequate security and safety. Use directional lighting, so that it does not intrude on nearby properties. Remember that high levels of lighting waste both energy and money. Consider using infrared lighting for security. Be aware of the possible presence of sensitive ecology, such as bat roosts and bird nesting areas, on site and position lighting accordingly to reduce adverse impacts (see Section 4.4.2).

3.3.3   Site security

Many environmental offences are based on strict liability, with little or no defence available. Contractors can be held liable for environmental damage even when it is caused by vandals.

Site security is an important component of good environmental management. Often, vandals cause damage that harms the environment by:

- opening taps on tanks containing fuel, or cutting fuel lines
- tipping out other liquids from drums and containers
- damaging/stealing raw materials
- playing on plant – damaging it and using it to cause damage
- spraying graffiti or fly posting on site hoardings
- destroying works in progress
- setting materials/waste on fire.

Also, rural areas may suffer from vandalism and especially theft, as their remote location provides time for thieves to remove plant and equipment without disturbance. The need for a manned presence in a remote location often is as important as in an urban setting.

> Help to reduce vandalism by securing the site, and moving valuable items and those prone to theft from public view. Store these goods in a locked container (Figure 3.10) or storage area.

A secure site helps ensure the safety of the community, particularly children, as construction sites are dangerous places. Education through school visits can help prevent children trespassing onto site.

Figure 3.10   Locked fuel tanks (courtesy BAM Nuttall)

Suggested security measures	
Site boundary	
Secure the site boundary using perimeter fencing and high quality locks on gates. Solid barriers (eg hoardings) are more difficult to scale than chain link fences and prevent casual surveillance by prospective thieves	
Do not stack materials against the inside or outside of a site boundary/fence as this can provide an opportunity for vandals and thieves to scale it	
Position fuel tanks, hazardous materials and waste away from the site boundary to deter theft and arson	

Suggested security measures	✓
Within site	
Ensure that potentially hazardous materials are well-secured and where possible located away from watercourses. For storage containers with a capacity in excess of 200 litres it is a legal requirement and also good practice, to lock fuel outlets when they are not in use, and provide secondary containment for oil in storage (eg bunds)	
Secure and immobilise plant and equipment overnight to prevent vandalism	
If the site is large or at high risk from trespassers install deterrents such as lights, warning notices, 24-hour security guards, alarm systems and closed circuit television (CCTV)	
Monitor movement of people on and off site by using site passes or swipe cards	
Position the site manager's office so that it has a good view of the site	
Inform local police about the site and ask for their advice on security	
Consult the Fire Service or advice on storing fuel and flammable materials on site	
If the site experiences a problem such as vandalism or graffiti, ensure that appropriate clean-up/repair is undertaken promptly, to discourage further problems from occurring	

3.4 INCIDENT PREPAREDNESS AND RESPONSE

The likelihood of an incident can be minimised by effective planning through development of a site pollution incident response plan. The plan needs to identify the on-site risks and appropriate responses. Suitable equipment, such as spill kits, oil booms and absorbent material, should be held at appropriate locations on site. An effective pollution incident response plan relies on the following elements:

- identification of all possible emergency scenarios
- effective planning, eg availability of booms, spills kits at appropriate locations
- identification of receptors/pathways (eg surface water drains/river. Receptors and pathways are described further in **Section 4.3.4**)
- identification and dissemination of contact numbers (see the following section)
- definition of site-based staff responsibilities
- appropriate site-based staff training
- exercise of incident scenarios – spill drills
- availability of suitable spill kits at appropriate locations on the site
- implement lessons learnt from previous incidents.

Incident response plan

Ensure that all appropriate site staff are aware of the company's site emergency procedure(s) (eg spillage, leakage, fire, explosion and flooding), that drain covers and spill kits are available, and they know how to use them. An incident response procedure (see **Figure 3.11**) should be based around the principle of:

STOP CONTAIN NOTIFY CLEAN-UP INVESTIGATE

Contact details that should be readily available:

- list of site-based staff and subcontractor offices
- the company's environmental representative
- Fire Service/Police (999)
- environmental regulator (Environment Agency, SEPA, NRW, NIEA)
- spill clean-up contractors
- local authority environmental health department
- sewerage provider
- equipment suppliers (skip hire for waste disposal)
- liquid waste disposal contractors
- local residents, the public and neighbouring business that could be affected.

Responsibilities

Make sure everyone knows who is responsible for:

- taking charge at the scene
- reporting to the site manager/environmental advisor
- reporting to the appropriate environmental regulators (Environment Agency, SEPA, NRW, NIEA)
- recording events as an incident record
- regularly checking that contents of the spill kits are complete
- communicating with the media.

Spill kits

Usually spill kits consisting of equipment to contain and absorb spills on land and water, are ideal for dealing with spillages. Obtain them from a reputable supplier and make sure they are specific to the oils and chemicals that are on site. At the start of the project it is important to assess the number and deployment of kits for quick access across site. The contents of a spill kit will depend on the project, but are likely to include:

- absorbent granules, pads and socks

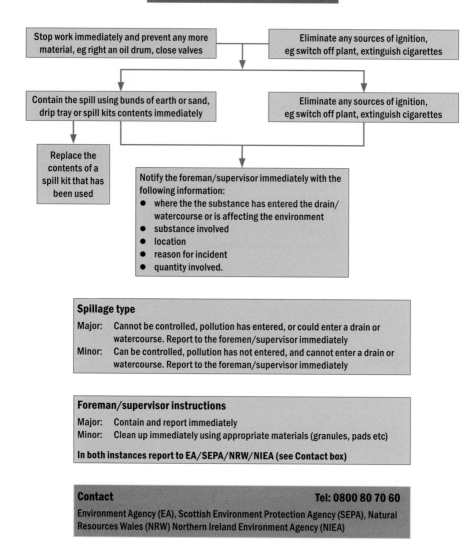

Stop – Contain – Notify

Stop work immediately and prevent any more material, eg right an oil drum, close valves

Eliminate any sources of ignition, eg switch off plant, extinguish cigarettes

Contain the spill using bunds of earth or sand, drip tray or spill kits contents immediately

Eliminate any sources of ignition, eg switch off plant, extinguish cigarettes

Replace the contents of a spill kit that has been used

Notify the foreman/supervisor immediately with the following information:
- where the the substance has entered the drain/ watercourse or is affecting the environment
- substance involved
- location
- reason for incident
- quantity involved.

Spillage type

Major: Cannot be controlled, pollution has entered, or could enter a drain or watercourse. Report to the foremen/supervisor immediately

Minor: Can be controlled, pollution has not entered, and cannot enter a drain or watercourse. Report to the foreman/supervisor immediately

Foreman/supervisor instructions

Major: Contain and report immediately

Minor: Clean up immediately using appropriate materials (granules, pads etc)

In both instances report to EA/SEPA/NRW/NIEA (see Contact box)

Contact   **Tel: 0800 80 70 60**

Environment Agency (EA), Scottish Environment Protection Agency (SEPA), Natural Resources Wales (NRW) Northern Ireland Environment Agency (NIEA)

Write up report of incident to be retained in site records including:
- date, time, location of spill
- substance(s) involved
- action taken to contain it
- lessons learnt.

Figure 3.11   Example incident response procedure

- string
- floating booms
- PPE, ie gloves, goggles and overalls
- drain covers/blockers
- polythene sheeting and bags.

Spill kits should be stored in a marked bag or wheelie bin (**Figure 3.12**) in a well-signposted location and protected to prevent damage from the weather. It is best to store them near to where they may be needed. Ensure that if materials from the spill kit are used that they are replaced immediately. Once equipment from a spill kit has been used it will need to be disposed of carefully. Some equipment may be hazardous/special waste and must be disposed of in accordance with legislation.

Figure 3.12   Spill response station (courtesy BAM Nuttall)

Table 3.3 provides detail of the types of spillages likely on construction sites and those materials that can be used to deal with them. This is followed by further guidance on the products.

Use of spill kit products

Universal/maintenance spill materials are designed to absorb and contain non-aggressive liquids and chemicals whether oil or water based. They are used for a wide range of liquids such as oils, coolants, paints, solvents, diesel and mild acids and alkalis. Some of these sorbent products are particularly useful for petrol spills because they stop the spill from releasing any more petrol vapours and make the spill safer. They are not suitable for use with aggressive chemicals.

Table 3.3   Common site spills and mitigation actions

Potential pollutant on site or spilt	Oil only	Oil and water	Concrete/cement/ Bentonite	Aggressive chemicals	Less aggressive chemicals (eg solvents)	Silt	Acids/alkalis
Type of spill kit/spill materials							
Universal/maintenance spill materials (eg spill kits, sawdust, granules)	Y	N	N	N	Y	N	N
Hydrocarbon/oil only sorbents (eg pads, booms, pillows	Y	Y	N	N	N	N	N
Chemical spills materials	Y	N	N	Y	Y	N	Y
Neutralisers	N	N	N	Y	N	N	Y
Bioremediation agents	Y	Y	N	N	Y	N	N
Surface cleaners/degreasers	Y	Y	N	N	N	N	N
Sand	Y	Y	N	N	N	N	N
Absorbent granules (should be suitable for substance)	Y	N	N	N	Y	N	Y
Drip trays (should only be made out of material suitable for substances to be contained)	Y	Y	N	Y	Y	N	Y
Plant nappies	Y	Y	N	N	N	N	N
Reusable drain seals	Y	Y	Y	N	Y	Y	N
Bentonite drain seals	Y	Y	Y	Y	Y	Y	Y
Oil booms	Y	Y	N	N	N	N	N
Fence booms	N	Y	Y	N	N	Y	N
Geotextile fence	N	N	Y	N	N	Y	N
Straw bales	N	N	Y	N	N	Y	N

Note that checks should be carried out with suppliers to ensure that the spill materials are appropriate for the substance.

Drip trays and plant nappies are used under static and portable plant to prevent leaks and drips contaminating the ground and/or water. Drip trays or similar should always be used during refuelling operations. Drip trays and plant nappies do not replace the legal requirements for oil storage.

Oil/hydrocarbon only spill kits only soak up oil and will float on water. They are ideal for mopping up spills on water such as lakes, rivers, ditches, oil bunds and in wet conditions. They are suitable for use with all fuels and hydrocarbons.

Bioremediation agents can sometimes break down an oil spill so that it becomes less polluting. They can be used to clean up oil spills but they should not be applied without prior approval from the environmental regulator. These products may take some time to be effective, especially in cold weather. Check that the bioremediation product being bought does not contain any pollutants that could make matters worse.

Surface cleaners and degreasers can be used to clean and wash oil off hard surfaces such as yards. However, these products are polluting and the wash-off water from these activities should not be discharged to land, groundwater or to surface water. Detergents

During site inspections review spill kit to ensure they are complete and include the most effective materials to be able to deal with potential pollution incidents on site.

can also cause interceptors to be ineffective as they cause the oil and water to form an emulsion, which bypass the interceptor system.

Chemical spill kits are designed to deal with all chemicals, including aggressive chemicals such as caustics, acids, solvents, oils and fuels.

Socks are particularly useful for forming a ring around spills to act as an absorbent barrier and to absorb spill.

If a major spill takes place that requires the use of spill kit equipment or an oil boom, contractors should immediately notify the appropriate environmental regulator about the spill. It is always good practice to inform the regulator of the incident if in any doubt of the potential damage caused by a spill.

The UK environmental incident hot line is **0800 80 70 60.**

Pads and rolls are used to absorb spilt liquids and can be used on land or water. Also, pads can be placed into drip trays to catch leaks/drips from machinery.

Marine booms are much larger barriers than socks and there are several different types. Oil booms can be linked to provide containment – some are also absorbent. Fence booms can be used to capture silt and wet concrete spills.

Cushions have great absorption capacity. They are particularly useful where there is the greatest concentration of spill. Also, they can be placed into drip trays to catch leaks/drips from machinery.

Oil spill – ground contamination (courtesy Kier)

3.4

Background

Refurbishment of social housing near to a river, with temporary power provided to the small site office and storage compound by a power unit containing a generator and a fully bunded fuel tank.

Issue

The unit was delivered to site direct from the manufacturer. It ran for several months before a leak was discovered in both the tank and the base of the bund. The leaking fuel soaked into the ground and eventually found its way into the river.

Site-based staff were able to deal with the fuel that had found its way into the river effectively and quickly, but the clean-up of the contained soil and groundwater took several months.

Pollution prevention measure

The ground contamination was cleaned up using appropriate measures. However, to stop this type of incident occurring again:

- introduce a generator log book, which includes an inspection checklist to be completed daily
- make it a company requirement that refuelling can only be carried out by a named, competent member of site-based staff.

Lessons learnt

- check that fuel storage tanks and bowsers and all associated pipe work are in good order before filling
- ensure that fuel storage tanks and bowsers and all associated pipework are regularly checked for leaks
- monitor fuel use – an abnormally high rate of consumption may indicate that the fuel storage tank is leaking
- report pollution incidents promptly to the environmental regulator and 'near misses' to management.

4 Environmental issues

4.1 ECOLOGY, PROTECTED SPECIES AND HABITAT

4.1.1 Introduction

Ecology is the study of wildlife and the interaction of different species with each other and their environment. The term 'wildlife' describes all naturally-occurring plants and animals (including mammals, birds, fish, reptiles, amphibians and insects) and 'habitat' describes the characteristics of the natural area where these species live. This could be, for example, a section of riverbank, an area of woodland or a hedgerow in an inner city park.

In the UK, the conservation of wildlife and natural features is the responsibility of the Statutory Nature Conservation Organisation (SNCO) for the relevant region:

Table 4.1   *UK Statutory Nature Conservation Organisations (SNCOs)*

Conservation body	Contact number
Natural England	0300 060 3900
Natural Resources Wales	0300 065 3000
Northern Ireland Environment Agency	0845 302 0008
Scottish Natural Heritage	01463 725 000

The remit of the SNCO includes providing ecological advice (such as consultation during planning), promoting biodiversity, conserving designated ecological, geological and geomorphological sites and protected species.

There is also a range of non-governmental organisations (NGO) that have a remit to conserve wildlife. These include wildlife trusts, and special interest groups such as badger, bat and bird societies (eg the Royal Society for the Protection of Birds [RSPB], and the Bat Conservation Trust [BCT]) and local wildlife groups.

4.1.2 Why is it important to consider ecology, species and habitats?

The natural environment supports all life through interrelated systems that support society in many ways. Some of these are obvious (such as pollination of crops), some may not be realised and many are not fully understood by scientists. Ecology has an intrinsic value to society, whether as part of complex system that supports humans, or the value it adds on a daily basis.

Due to past practices and the potential effect that construction has on ecology, the level of protection given to wildlife is increasing through legal controls and contract conditions. The identification of wildlife within a site (and surrounding it) needs to be undertaken at the planning stage of a project to ensure the required surveys can be carried out and the correct protection measures can be implemented. This is important to avoid both delays to the project programme and the extra costs or fines that could be incurred.

The public is aware of impacts construction projects can have on the natural environment. Many projects are under the spotlight on environmental grounds and the public will notice poor environmental practice. So it is important for good public relations to have proper regard for ecological issues on site.

Potential effects on ecology

There are numerous potential effects that construction sites can have on ecology, but these can be generally classified as:

- direct effects on ecology at site level, eg pollution of a watercourse on site, removal of habitat, killing of individual flora or fauna
- indirect effects as a result of construction processes/activities, eg deforestation for timber materials, downstream water pollution of a habitat.

Works should avoid disturbance to species during particularly sensitive times, eg during hibernation, mating and nesting seasons. If this is not considered early enough in the project programme, disruption may be caused. When damage has occurred, negotiating with the SNCOs (see **Section 4.1.1**) and repairing the damage takes time, can cause delays to the programme, and will be at the construction company's cost.

To avoid these pitfalls, consider surveys that may need to be undertaken (and when), consents required and any mitigation requirements early and build these into the project programme to limit disruption.

Potential causes of damage to ecology on site

Those working in construction should take all possible steps to avoid having an impact on wildlife and habitats, and to protect particular species and designated sites (eg Site of Special Scientific Interest, SSSI, or Area of Special Scientific Interest, ASSI). It is important to take a responsible attitude to the natural environment as a whole. Be aware that most activities during construction can have a direct, temporary or permanent effect on the surrounding ecology, such as:

- pollution to surface water, groundwater and marine environments

- works altering inundation (flooding) regimes of habitats
- the destruction of places inhabited by flora and fauna (this is a feature of most developments)
- interruptions to the movement of wildlife
- habitat fragmentation or vegetation damage
- removal of hedgerows and other vegetation that may require legal consent
- high noise and vibration levels disturbing nearby ecology
- changes in lighting
- damage, removal or burial of important rock formations or landforms
- dust generation may affect protected plant species
- silt and soil runoff that may affect plant species that may then affect the animals that depend on them.

Also, be aware that works on site may affect ecology off site and consideration should be given to the surrounding area and any protective or preventative measures that should be implemented. For example, it is an offence to disturb nesting birds irrespective of where they are and whether they are on or off site.

Managing potential effects

A responsible attitude should be adopted to ensure construction activities cause the least damage to the surrounding natural environment. Where possible, opportunities should be taken to enhance the natural environment through appropriate habitat creation that improves biodiversity and promotes positive construction practice.

It is good practice to employ an experienced ecologist to advise the project on:

- identification of flora and fauna and evaluation of ecological features, such as woodland and wetlands especially should there be potential for protected habitats or species to be found
- understanding and advising on ecological constraints
- developing proposals for mitigation or enhancement and suitable methods of work to complete it

> Remember that ecology is a specialised subject, and no two sites are the same, so it is important to obtain professional advice.

- identifying opportunities for enhancing the ecological value of the site
- relevant legislation, planning policy and guidance.

4.1.3 Legal requirements

Disturbing protected species or damaging the places where they live can result in prosecution under a range of legislation. The fine for noncompliance varies according to the species and the habitat and the type of damage caused. For example, if protected species such as bats, badgers, or great crested newts are disturbed, fines may be imposed at £5000 per animal. Also, there is scope for the confiscation of any vehicles or other equipment used to commit the offence, and criminal record and custodial sentence for those involved.

Designated sites are protected against certain activities and carry legal duties concerning how such areas are to be managed and safeguarded. Level of legal protection, restricted activities and penalties for offences depend upon the designation, the ecological sensitivity and the offence. For example, SSSIs are protected against, among other things, intentional or reckless damage, disturbance or destruction of land known to be an SSSI or intentional or reckless disturbance of the wildlife in an SSSI. Such an offence could carry a **fine of up to £5000** in a Magistrates court or **unlimited fine** or **six months in prison** in the Crown Court.

Contract or planning conditions may state that certain trees must remain undamaged. These trees may be subject to a Tree Preservation Order (TPO), be within a conservation area, or related to a former planning permission. Any works that may affect a protected tree should first be approved by the local authority. Replacing damaged mature trees is expensive – a 10 m high tree may cost £2000, plus extra expense for delivery, planting and several years' maintenance.

> A water company was fined £250 000 for allowing untreated sewage to enter a brook running through a nature reserve. The scale of the penalty imposed by the Crown Court reflected the new sentencing guidelines for environmental offences (Sentencing Council, 2014).

4.1.4 Effective integration of ecology

Wildlife surveys

It is possible to organise works, so that ecological issues are dealt with appropriately, legally, in-line with good practice, cost effectively and at the right time of year to enable seasonal surveys without undue delays to the project programme.

To achieve this consult an ecologist for advice first to enable the ecological constraints to be identified at the start of the project. Surveys are seasonally constrained, so ensuring these constraints are known early on, enables them to be programmed in appropriately.

In the majority of cases, ecological surveys will be required in order for a project to receive planning permission. Even if planning permission has been received legislation or planning conditions may require that further surveys are carried out to assess the impacts on specially protected species and/or habitats and/or a need to obtain licences to work with or disturb species and/or habitats. A project can be delayed while waiting for the correct time of year to undertake a wildlife survey of the site and/or for a licence to be applied and granted.

A more detailed version of the protected species survey calendar is accessible from **www.ciria.org/egpos**

Figure 4.1 provides an indication of when to undertake wildlife surveys for frequently encountered protected species before work begins. This should help to minimise the risk of delays. Some surveys may only be carried out at particular times of the year by a professional ecologist, and some surveys require an appropriate survey licence to be held by the ecologist.

Important considerations

There are two situations when ecological issues may arise on site:

1   **Before works – where surveys have been carried out before works start and species or areas of the site have been identified for particular protection.** In these situations, an experienced ecologist would have conducted site surveys and desk studies, including reviewing the local biodiversity action plan (LBAP) and any special designation (for example a nature reserve) that may be assigned to the site. This information would enable an assessment of the ecological constraints to be identified and impacts on the ecology of the site to be mitigated. Site staff would be made aware of the special working methods they would need to follow to protect any sensitive species or habitats and of any areas or features that should be avoided by traffic movements, materials storage or other impacts from the site. Working practices and programmes can be drawn up with these aspects in mind. The experienced ecologist will be able to advise on the need to obtain licences to allow certain activities to occur.

2   **During works – where protected species are discovered when the contractor is already on site and works have begun.** In these situations, work must be stopped immediately, and the site manager must immediately obtain expert advice on how to proceed. Consultation with the SNCOs may have to take place to discuss the best way to continue. This may create delays to the programme and opportunities for mitigation may be limited when the design is fixed and works have begun. In some instances this may require some aspects of the development to be re-designed.

4.1.5   Dealing with protected species

Many animals, plants and birds are protected throughout or for part of the year by legislation. Work may have to be adapted or delayed until such a time that the development will cause no adverse effect on them or the places where they live. Work may be subject to licences issued by the SNCOs if it is considered that the planned activities could affect protected species or habitats.

Different regions across the UK operate different schedules of protected species through their respective legislation.

Survey period	January	February	March	April	May	June	July	August	September	October	November	December	
Dormice Surveys May to October													Dormice are orangey-brown with a white belly and furry tail. They are nocturnal and live in woodland and hedges
Bats Roost surveys May to September													Bats are found in rural and urban areas and use different roosting places for resting, breeding and hibernating
Reptiles Surveys April to September													There are six species of reptile in the UK (common lizards, sand lizards, slow worms, adders, grass snakes and smooth snakes)
Great crested newts Pond surveys March to June													All newts are amphibians and great crested newts have bright orangey-yellow bellies with black spots
Breeding birds Surveys March to August													Birds, including rare species, may be found breeding on construction sites. Nesting sites should only be inspected by experienced ecologists and work should stop in the immediate area
Otters Surveys all year, when water levels are low													Otters live along watercourses and occur in both rural and urban areas, including major cities
Water voles Surveys March to October													Water voles have chestnut brown fur, a round face and a short furry tail. They are found in slow-flowing rivers, ditches, dikes and around lakes and ponds with steep banks and vegetation
Badgers Surveys March to September													Badgers are up to a metre long and live in groups in underground setts. They are nocturnal and leave well-worn paths, dungpits and scratching posts in their territories

Figure 4.1   Protected species survey calendar (after Newton et al, 2011). For full details of various species, and their requirements, please consult Newton et al (2011)

These organisations should be consulted for advice before works start to avoid potentially expensive delays. SNCOs require time to review licence applications, which can vary between organisations. Planning permission is usually required before an application for a licence can be made.

To obtain a full list of species protected under legislation and to assist dealing with them on site see Newton *et al* (2011). If it is suspected that any protected animal may be affected by the site works stop and obtain specialist advice before continuing.

Figure 4.2   Pipistrelle bat

Some of the important species that may be encountered are as follows.

Bats

Bats roost in a variety of localities in both urban and rural areas, these include:

- holes and cracks in trees
- in roofs and walls of buildings
- under bridges
- underground caves
- disused railway tunnels.

Bats hibernate between October and April and breed and rear their young between May and August. If bats are likely to be encountered, a survey will be required by a suitably licensed ecologist to establish the location and size of the roost. Only suitably licensed ecologists are allowed legally to enter known bat roosts or to capture or handle bats. It is illegal to injure, kill, capture or disturb a bat, or to damage trees, buildings or other places used for roosting, even if the roost is unoccupied at the time.

Dormice

Dormice are typically associated with woodland with dense under-storey and species-rich hedgerows with good connectivity to surrounding habitats. They can also be found in bramble scrub. Dormice and their nests are protected against disturbance, killing and injury, damage and destruction of a breeding site, and damage and obstruction of a place of rest. No native dormice are found in Northern Ireland.

Amphibians

Great crested newts (GCN) (**Figure 4.3**) and natterjack toads (**Figure 4.6**) are fully protected by law.

GCNs can be found predominantly in ponds in rural, urban and suburban areas. They are nocturnal and spend most of their time within grass, scrub, woodland and under logs within 500 m of a water body. They spawn in ponds and slow moving water bodies between March and June. Other species of newt that could be encountered on site are the smooth (**Figure 4.4**) or palmate (**Figure 4.5**).

Figure 4.3   *Great crested newt (courtesy Scottish Natural Heritage)*

Figure 4.4   *Smooth newt (courtesy Scottish Natural Heritage)*

Figure 4.5   *Palmate newt (courtesy Scottish Natural Heritage)*

Natterjack toads are extremely rare in Britain (**Figure 4.6**). Both are European protected species, so any works affecting them is illegal without a licence. If found or suspected on site all works must stop immediately and expert advice sought.

Natterjack toads are found predominantly in sandy habitats such as coastal sand dunes and grazing marshes or lowland heaths. In Cumbria and Scotland populations are also thriving on upland moor, salt marshes and post-industrial sites.

Figure 4.6   *Natterjack toad (courtesy Scottish Natural Heritage)*

Reptiles

All reptiles are protected and should not be killed or injured. In the UK there are six native species of land-dwelling reptiles:

- common lizard
- sand lizard
- slow-worm
- adder
- grass snake
- smooth snake.

Figure 4.7   Adder (courtesy BAM Nuttall)

Reptiles hibernate in winter but are active the rest of the year. Mating takes place between April and June and the young are born between July and October. Reptiles can be found throughout the UK and are typically found in dense grassland, or scrub with open areas where they can bask, among vegetation on railway embankments and hedgerows. They can also be found sheltering under rocks and logs. It is illegal to kill or injure common lizards, slow-worms, grass snakes and adders (**Figure 4.7**). Sand lizards and smooth snakes are European protected species so any works affecting them is illegal without a licence. If reptiles are found, or are likely to be found, stop work immediately and consult an ecologist for advice.

Badgers

Badgers and their setts (**Figures 4.8** and **4.9**) are protected under legislation. It is an offence to directly disturb a badger sett, or to carry out works close to a badger sett that could cause a disturbance, without a licence from the relevant SNCO.

Badgers are widespread throughout the UK and can be found living in:

- woodland
- road and railway embankments
- refuse tips
- under buildings
- in-root systems/hollow trees.

Setts are a network of tunnels and chambers underground. The entrance is visible above ground

Figure 4.8   Badger

and can be identified by a rounded or flattened, oval-shaped hole and the presence of large spoil mounds.

Types of activity where consideration should be given regarding obtaining a licence within certain distances of sett entrances:

- 30 m – using very heavy machinery (generally tracked vehicles)
- 20 m – using lighter machinery (generally wheeled vehicles), particularly for any digging operation
- 10 m – light work such as hand digging or scrub clearance.

Some activities may cause disturbance at greater distances (such as using explosives or pile driving) and these should be given individual consideration.

Badger licences should be obtained from the relevant SNCO, if site activity is likely to interfere with a badger sett for example:

- damaging or destroying a badger sett
- obstructing any entrance to a sett
- disturbing a badger when it is occupying a sett.

If a badger or a sett is discovered after works have started, work must stop immediately and expert advice must be sought.

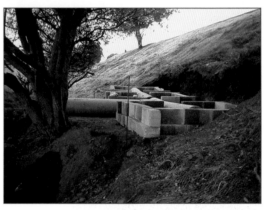

Figure 4.9 ***Badger sett construction (courtesy BAM Nuttall)***

Water voles

Water voles (**Figure 4.10**) can easily be confused with rats. Water voles can be found on the banks of surface water features in shallow burrows, often close to the ground surface, which can extend up to five metres from the water edge near or below the water-line in various locations.

There should be no construction works or equipment within five metres of a watercourse, including cabins and plant, and especially generator sets as the vibrations caused by these can lead to disturbance through the ground.

Figure 4.10 *Water vole*

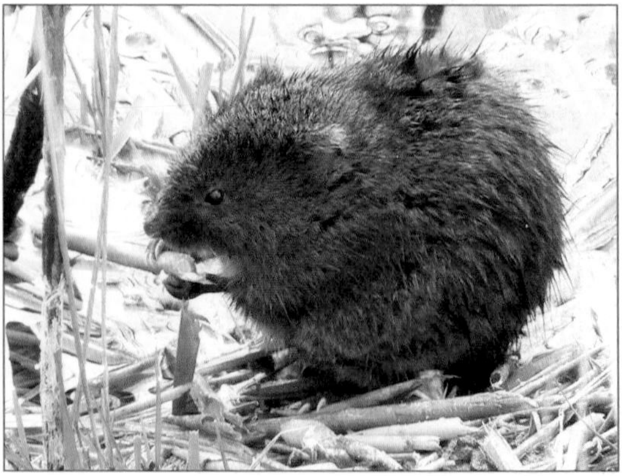

Water voles may be found in the banks near to:

- slow-flowing rivers
- streams
- ditches

- dykes
- around ponds and lakes.

Water voles tend to be more active during the day and are active all year round. Water voles and their burrows are legally protected against damage and disturbance. In Scotland only the water vole's place of shelter is protected. If water voles are found after works have started, all works must stop immediately to avoid breaking the law, and expert advice must be sought. Water voles are not found in Northern Ireland.

Figure 4.11   Bird nesting in scaffolding (courtesy Galliford Try plc)

Nesting birds

All birds and their nests (**Figure 4.11**) are protected under legislation. Some rare species, eg barn owl, some birds of prey and kingfishers, are further protected against disturbance. To avoid disturbance to nesting birds, the programming of tree and hedge removal should fall outside of the nesting season (usually March to August inclusive). Where this is not possible, an ecologist should check vegetation for signs of breeding bird activity before clearance.

Figure 4.12   Fox

Birds often use building sites as breeding areas including nesting on scaffolding or machinery. If this occurs the equipment cannot be used until the birds have finished nesting and any young have left the nest. The area may also need to be sealed off to prevent any disturbance. If nesting birds are found, consult the SNCOs for further advice.

Foxes

All mammals including foxes (**Figure 4.12**) have a level of protection under legislation. Fox earths should not be destroyed until it is certain that they are unoccupied. Holes should not be filled between March and May as cubs are likely to be below ground. If a fox earth is discovered after works have started, work must stop immediately and expert advice must be sought before undertaking any further works. Be aware that a licence is required to close badger setts even if occupied by foxes.

Other species

Other protected species include red squirrel, pine marten, wildcat, otter, some fish species, marine mammals, invertebrates. In addition, a number of notable species also warrant consideration when mitigating ecological impacts and so ecological advice should always be sought.

Management of swift colony during regeneration works (courtesy Kier Living)

4.1

Kier Living worked to regenerate the Windmill Estate in Fulbourn, Cambridgeshire by demolishing a large number of 1960s houses and replacing them with modern new homes for social landlord Accent Nene. The eaves of the old flat-roofed houses provides extremely attractive nesting sites for swifts that like to breed in inaccessible cavities high up in buildings. Swift numbers in the UK have steadily declined in recent years – partly due to the way new houses are being designed.

To ensure the swifts were not lost from the village, Kier Living, with guidance from the Swift Conservation Organisation and the local authority provided large numbers of specially-made nesting boxes throughout the new estate. One type is simply fitted to the gable, while another is built into the cavity wall.

A consultant ecologist was employed throughout the summer period to monitor the swifts to discover the size of the colony and the buildings where they nested. This meant Kier Living could be sure all the birds had safely completed breeding and migrated before they started the second phase of demolitions at the end of the summer.

Translocation of species

Translocation should be considered as the last resort and only occur when habitat damage is anticipated and unavoidable, but the species concerned can be moved off the site and reinstated in suitable habitat elsewhere. Where translocation is required this typically forms part of the site preparation works and is carried out by specialists. Translocation often needs to take place within specific time periods (**Figure 4.1**), and may influence the project programme. Both aftercare and monitoring of translocated species are essential. Without planning and consideration, translocation may become an expensive process.

Warning signs

As always, the best thing to do is to plan ahead and consult an ecologist early on to prevent problems arising. However, some signs indicate that there are serious problems on site:

- bats or other nocturnal animals being seen during daylight hours or found on the ground near to the site
- injured birds, smashed eggs, young unaccompanied fledglings
- dead fish floating in watercourses affected by works.

If these signs, or others that indicate animals are being harmed or injured, are encountered, works must stop immediately and advice sought from an ecologist.

On site

Ecological advice at the earliest stage is always beneficial. Initial ecological input will involve a desk study of existing ecological data of the site and surrounding area, analysis of aerial photographs to facilitate assessment of likely ecological receptors, and a site walkover to map and note the ecological constraints and opportunities within the site. Where appropriate, stakeholder and consultee liaison should be carried out. Further ecological surveys should be identified and programmed in, appropriate both for the survey season and for the timeline of the proposed works.

These measures apply to all developments including private developments and smaller schemes to ensure that impacts on ecology are adequately addressed and legal requirements are met.

Relevant information may then need to be submitted to the LPA. It is important to ensure that contractors are provided with relevant details.

Figure 4.13   Wildlife Barriers (courtesy Skanska)

Usually, particular working practices to protect the ecological features (**Figure 4.13**) will have been recommended to adopt on site. Where these are given, follow the advice. If no recommendations are given, consult an environmental advisor or the person assigned with environmental responsibility in the site environmental plan, such as the Ecological Clerk of Works (ECoW), or ask for advice from an experienced ecologist.

Before work begins, identify and securely fence off any sensitive habitats (**Figure 4.14**) and restrict the movement of workers to designated areas. This will help to minimise the damage

that may be caused. For many categories of wildlife, for example nesting birds and roosting bats, the timing of work will be important, so correct scheduling may avoid problems (**Figure 4.1**). Liaise with the SNCOs and with third parties such as local environmental/wildlife groups for advice.

Communicate any areas of concern and PLC conditions to site-based staff, eg during site inductions or toolbox talks, to ensure the

Figure 4.14   Great crested newt fencing (courtesy Brookfield Multiplex)

potential issues are understood. As required, adopt a programme of monitoring before and during construction through to site restoration. Ensure that the monitoring process includes action to be taken in the event of problems.

4.1.6   Noxious and invasive non-native species

Noxious plants are those that can pose a risk to human or environmental health because of the chemicals they contain. Care should be taken when in contact with such plants or when removing them from site.

Invasive Non-Native Species (INNS) are those plants and animals that are not native to the UK and have been introduced into the

It is illegal to cause the spread of invasive species.	

environment. Often INNS species out-compete native species due to lack of natural controls and do not support native wildlife. INNS species are a complex issue affecting regions throughout the UK.

Ecology is adversely affected through the spreading of noxious and invasive species and it is an offence to cause their spread in the wild. Note that species may be added so it is important to keep up-to-date with lists contained within the legislation.

If noxious or invasive plants are found on site it is the responsibility of the site manager to take the following action:

● cordon off the area to prevent any inadvertent spreading (**Figure 4.15**)

● notify the environmental regulator that the plant is present

● ensure any vehicles that have been in the affected area have their wheels/tracks thoroughly washed before leaving the area of the site where the plant is located

● water used to clean vehicles must be controlled to prevent the spread of the plant (through seeds, rhizomes, fragments etc).

Figure 4.15   Japanese knotweed signage (courtesy Kier)

For advice for the most effective treatment and disposal of the plant to prevent spreading, giving the particular circumstances on site consult a specialist and/or the regulator.

Where invasive animals are noted, such as killer shrimp and signal crayfish, these should be reported to the monitoring authority, such as the regional environment regulator. Any waders, pond nets, equipment etc that may have been in contact with contaminated water must be thoroughly washed, disinfected and dried.

Following specialist advice, approval for the proposed control methods should be sought from the environmental regulator.

4.1.7 Habitats

Habitats are defined as areas possessing uniformity of landform, vegetation, climate or any other quality assumed to be important. Usually, in terms of site assessment and management, it is uniformity (or diversity) of vegetation that characterises a habitat. Habitats are usually formed naturally although they can be man-made, eg through habitat creation, translocation (**Figure 4.17**). There are several types of habitat:

- coastal and marine
- freshwater
- grassland
- heathland
- hedgerows and individual trees
- road and railway embankments
- soil
- urban areas
- wetland
- woodland and scrub.

Japanese knotweed (*Fallopia japonica*) (Figure 4.16) grows densely, shades out other plants, reduces biodiversity, and penetrates asphalt, walls, and foundations. It is a destructive plant that has been known to re-grow through tarmac and paving as well as disrupting underground structures and services.

Giant hogweed (*Heracleum mantegazzianum*) has poisonous sap and extreme care should be taken when removing it. Relevant personal protective equipment (PPE) should be provided as the sap can burn and irritate skin. Appropriate PPE should be provided if there is any chance of the sap being spread or vaporised through cutting.

Himalayan balsam (*Impatiens glandulifera*) grows densely along riverbanks and in wetland areas, shades out other plants, and reduces biodiversity. It should be cut down when in flower to prevent the seed heads from forming and spraying their seeds further infesting the local area.

Figure 4.16   *Japanese knotweed (courtesy BAM Nuttall)*

The ecological richness of a habitat (its biodiversity) can be affected in many ways. Invasive plants such as Japanese knotweed can reduce biodiversity by out-competing other plant species. The effects of human activities on habitats include spillages of hazardous substances on the ground and into water, felling trees or removing hedgerows, site clearance or demolition.

Measures to reinstate any habitats damaged during the works may form part of the contract or planning conditions. Such measures have to be planned in advance and may require specialist advice. There may be particular requirements in selecting the type of species for reinstating.

Figure 4.17   Artificial hibernacula (courtesy Skanska)

The insect hotel illustrated in **Figure 4.18** is just one of a growing number of examples of simple biodiversity enhancements that can be incorporated into projects being championed by a initiatives including CIRIA's BIG Challenge of 'do one thing' (see *Big Challenge* box on page 84 for further details).

Designated sites

Sites with important ecological attributes (including plant and animal species) or natural landforms can be given special protection that can be applied at the regional, national or international level according to their importance or rarity. Examples of designated sites (in alphabetical order) are:

Figure 4.18   Insect hotel (courtesy Brookfield Multiplex)

- Area of Outstanding Natural Beauty (AONB)
- Area of Special scientific Interest (ASSI) (Northern Ireland)
- County Wildlife Sites (CWS)
- Local Nature Reserve (LNR)
- National Nature Reserve (NNR)
- National Scenic Area (NSA) (Scotland)
- RAMSAR site (wetlands of international importance)
- Regionally Important Geological Sites (RIGS)
- Special Area of Conservation (SAC)

Management of Japanese knotweed (courtesy Willmott Dixon)

Site issues

About 1200 m² of Japanese knotweed was discovered on site within the footprint of a newly built school. It was found at a central town location resulting in difficult access/issues with lorry movements. During site investigations works Japanese knotweed was disturbed. It had been previously treated chemically resulting in dormant areas and mutated growth. The site levels need to be increased, so removing material via conventional treatments would add to cost of reinstatement.

There were several issues that needed to be considered:

- likely high landfill costs
- requirement for an environmental permit from the Environment Agency for screening operation
- client requirement for as much of the material as possible to remain on site
- warranty required on all works
- approximately 4500 m³ of material likely to be produced from excavations to clear the Japanese knotweed.

Methodology

An environmental permit was deployed (with a six week application process). Areas of Japanese knotweed were to be excavated to depth of rhizome/safe level and the resulting material to be processed through Enviroscreen 20-20XL.

Soils to be split in to three fractions with the following reuse detail:

- Fraction 1 – material greater than 75 mm in diameter (stone, concrete and brick) to be crushed for reuse anywhere on the site.
- Fraction 2 – material less than 75 mm in diameter (soil, stone etc) to pass through the process to remove all visible knotweed rhizome. Resulting clean soil can be used anywhere on site without restriction.
- Fraction 3 – material less than 20 mm in diameter (predominantly topsoil) to be buried on site behind the retailing wall with a minimum cap of 500 mm of clean soil.

Remediation

Screening works took four weeks on site. Fragmented asbestos sheeting was discovered during the process and removed under appropriate controls using correct PPE. Japanese knotweed was removed from up to five metres in some areas, while some areas were not excavated to exhaust knotweed rhizome due to angle of repose with neighbouring houses. Around 4000 m³ of soil was processed on site (removal costs of this volume would have exceeded £350 000). Only viable Japanese knotweed material was removed to landfill. The total volume removed was nine tons). The project was completed on time and on budget, with a total cost of screening works £89 500.

Lessons learnt

It was found that early planning is critical when Japanese knotweed is identified as this allow for more cost effective management methods to be adopted.

- Special Protection Area (SPA)
- Site of Importance for Nature Conservation (SINC)
- Site of Local Importance for Nature Conservation (SLINC)
- Site of Local Nature Conservation Importance (SLNCI)
- Site of Nature Conservation Interest (SNCI)
- Site of Special Scientific Interest (SSSI)
- World Heritage Site (WHS).

Always contact the SNCO for further guidance on designated sites.

It is an offence to carry out works on a designated site without the permission of the relevant nature conservation body. Often several months' notice is required before works begin. It is important to adhere to working methods once they have been agreed with the appropriate SNCO.

> **BIG Challenge**
>
> The BIG Challenge of 'do one thing' invites you to add one new biodiversity enhancement to your construction site, development or existing building.
>
> The biodiversity enhancement can be something simple, such as adding hanging baskets planted with native wildflowers, creating bug hotels, rain gardens, planted cycle locks or skip gardens. These measures can be a permanent feature of your development, or temporary during the construction phase that, when finished, could potentially be applied to the next site and enhanced further.
>
> For more information go to:
> **www.bigchallenge.info**

4.1.8   Natural features

Trees and hedgerows

Damage to trees and hedgerows may be caused either through direct physical injury to the branches, trunk or roots or by changing the soil or water character around the roots. This can arise from various actions including compaction (even one piece of machinery going over the root protection area can cause damage), raising soil levels, impervious covering around tree roots, raising the water table, hazardous spillages, soil stripping, or excavations. Refer to the checklist at the end of this section for more details (see also BS 5837:2012).

Tree protection

A TPO protects a single tree, group of trees or woodland. It protects trees from being topped, lopped or removed. Consent must be obtained before any work on a tree with a TPO is undertaken. Failure to gain permission is an offence and could result in a fine of up to £20 000. All trees located within a conservation area are protected.

The LPA department should be contacted before work starts on any protected trees. To gain permission to work on a tree(s) with a TPOs, complete and return a form obtained from the local authority outlining the intended work. The local authority then has up to two months to make a decision. During this time local residents can appeal against the work.

When a tree that has a TPO in force is dead, dying or dangerous, it can be felled without permission, but the local authority should always be consulted before any action is taken.

Before removing any trees on local authority land, the relevant authority needs to be contacted so that they can identify whether there is a need to place a provisional TPO on any of the tree(s) that may otherwise be damaged or removed during construction works.

Consideration also needs to be given to protected species (eg bats, breeding birds, invertebrates) as well as plants (eg lichens, mosses) that may be supported by the tree(s) and expert advice sought before works begin.

Hedgerow protection

Hedgerows in England and Wales are protected under legislation and there is a requirement to notify the LPA in whose area the hedgerow is situated. The removal of any hedge longer than 20 m requires planning permission. If the hedge is shown to be significant in terms of its age, environmental or historical importance, then the LPA can refuse such permission (after a six week determination period) and take further measures to protect the hedgerow.

Rocks and landforms

These are an important part of the UK's natural heritage. Some rock exposures and landforms will be SSSIs/ASSIs, but others may be locally important. If there is any doubt as to the importance of these features and how to protect them, contact the nature conservation bodies who will provide contact details for a local RIGS group.

4.1.9 Good practice checklists

What to look out for on site	
Protected species	
If found on site (or suspected to be on site) stop work and follow the required processes to manage them	
Consult a site ecologist before any works to mitigate or translocate are undertaken	
Invasive non-native species	
If found, or suspected to be, on site follow the required processes to manage them	
Consult an ecologist for advice before any works are undertaken	
Nesting birds	
If found, do not disturb or cut down trees or shrubs	

What to look out for on site	✓
To avoid accidental disturbance do not fell or clear any trees or shrubs between March and August	
Protect trees in or next to the working area from nuisance (ie noise and light pollution)	
Working near water	
Place a protective bund around ponds to prevent water pollution	
Dewatering can affect the ecology of wetlands around the site. Consider monitoring water levels during the works	
Put mitigation measures in place, eg silt fencing to protect water quality	
Avoiding damage to trees and hedgerows	
Check whether any trees on site are covered by a TPO and liaise with the local authority (local planning office in Northern Ireland)	
Consider the presence of protected species (eg bats, breeding birds, invertebrates) and consult an ecologist for advice	
Keep vehicles and plant away from trees and hedgerows	
Put up temporary fencing to mark out area around those that need to be protected	
Do not cut or damage any roots greater than 25 mm in diameter within the protected area	
Cut roots only with a clean hand saw, not a spade or mechanical digger	
Wrap damp sacking around any exposed roots until ready for backfilling	
Backfill holes with care, to ensure that roots are not damaged, and compact backfill lightly	
Do not store spoil or building materials within protected area or under tree canopy	
Keep toxic materials such as diesel and cement well away	
Always avoid damaging bark or branches	

4.1.10 Further reading

ANDERSON, P and GROUTAGE, P (2003) *Habitat translocation – a best practice guide*, C600, CIRIA, London (ISBN: 978-0-86017-600-8). Go to: **www.ciria.org**

BAKER, J, BEEBEE, T, BUCKLEY, J, GENT, T and ORCHARD, D (2010) *Amphibian habitat management handbook*, Amphibian and Reptile Conservation Trust, Dorset, UK. Go to: **http://tinyurl.com/kf3bpfd**

EDGAR, P, FOSTER, J and BAKER, J (2010) *Reptile habitat management handbook*, Amphibian and Reptile Conservation Trust, Dorset, UK. Go to: **http://tinyurl.com/kl8noqc**

ENVIRONMENT AGENCY (2013) *Managing Japanese Knotweed on development sites, version 3*, Environment Agency, Bristol. Go to: **http://tinyurl.com/o6yhagw**

WADE, M, BOOY, O and WHITE, V (2008) *Invasive species management for infrastructure managers and the construction industry*, C679, CIRIA, London (ISBN: 978-0-86017-679-4). Go to: **www.ciria.org**

4.1.11 Legislation

Legislation is constantly changing, including amendments and new legislation, and this varies between England, Wales, Scotland and Northern Ireland. If site staff are unsure on any environmental issue, contact the regional environmental regulator for advice.

Legislation	Key requirements	Applicable Nation(s)
The Wildlife and Natural Environment (Scotland) Act 2011	This act is divided into four parts covering protection of wildlife, designation of protected areas, public rights of way, and miscellaneous provisions. It sets out the system to define and control SSSIs and the best examples of natural heritage of wildlife habitats, geological features and landforms. It also makes provisions for the management of deer and the regulation of muirburn.	Scotland
The Nature Conservation (Scotland) Act 2004	Sets out the system to define and control SSSI or the best examples of Scottish natural heritage of wildlife habitats, geological features and landforms. Also makes provisions for the protection of land from weeds such as Japanese knotweed. Lists species protected from disturbance, injury, intentional destruction or sale, eg nesting birds.	Scotland
Town and Country Planning (Scotland) Act 1997	Restriction or protection of hedgerows in Scotland may be detailed during planning.	Scotland
Wild Mammals (Protection) Act (as amended, 1996)	Makes it an offence to harm any wild animal with intent or to inflict unnecessary suffering.	England
Protection of Badgers Act 1992	Makes it an offence to: • kill, injure or take a badger • cruelly ill-treat any badger • interfere with a badger sett.	England, Wales, Scotland
Wildlife and Countryside Act 1981 (as amended)	This Act (as amended) is the major legal instrument for wildlife protection in Britain. It is divided into four parts covering protection of wildlife, designation of protected areas, public rights of way, and miscellaneous provisions. It sets out the system to define and control SSSIs and the best examples of natural heritage of wildlife habitats, geological features and landforms. It also makes provisions for the protection of land from weeds such as Japanese knotweed and lists species protected from disturbance, injury, intentional destruction or sale, eg nesting birds.	England, Wales, Scotland
Weeds Act 1959 (as amended)	Requires the occupiers of land on which injurious weeds are growing to take action to prevent their spread. The Act specifies five such species Common ragwort, Spear thistle, Creeping field thistle, Broad leaved dock and Curled dock.	England, Wales, Scotland

Legislation	Key requirements	Applicable Nation(s)
Conservation of Habitats and Species Regulations, 2010 (as amended)	Allows for the designation of SACs and SPAs, collectively known as 'European Sites' and the protection of habitats and species listed in annexes.	England, Wales
The Environmental Damage (Prevention and Remediation) Regulations 2009 Environmental Damage (Prevention and Remediation) (Wales) Regulations 2009	Any environmental damage following activity on site should be remedied. If there is a risk of damage from any business activities, it must be prevented. The Regulations do not apply to environmental damage caused before they came into force. However, they are likely to be used only for the most serious cases of damage. Under the Regulations, environmental damage is: serious damage to surface water or groundwater contamination of land where there is a significant risk to human health serious damage to EU protected natural habitats and species or damage to SSSIs.	England, Wales
Environmental Liability (Scotland) Regulations 2009 (as amended) Environmental Liability (Prevention and Remediation) Regulations (Northern Ireland) 2009 (as amended)	If any business activities cause environmental damage then it should be remedied. If there is a risk of damage from business activities then it must be prevented. The Regulations do not apply to environmental damage caused before they came into force. However, they are likely to be used only for the most serious cases of damage. Under the Regulations, environmental damage is: serious damage to surface water or groundwater contamination of land where there is a significant risk to human health serious damage to EU protected natural habitats and species or damage to SSSIs/ASSIs.	Scotland, Northern Ireland
Town and Country Planning (Trees) Regulations 1999 (as amended) Town and Country Planning (Tree preservation order and trees in conservation areas) (Scotland) Regulations (2010)	These regulations make provision for the protection of trees. Key features include: • powers for local authorities to assign TPO status to single or groups of trees • local authorities have powers to vary and revoke TPOs • provide for circumstances when trees protected by TPOs can be topped, lopped or felled.	England, Wales Scotland
Hedgerow Regulations, 1997	To be protected, the hedgerow must: • run on agricultural land or common land, for example a village green, or land that runs alongside it • be on or bordering a nature reserve, or SSSI • be at least 30 years old and at least 20 m long. Garden hedges are not protected.	England, Wales
The Conservation (Natural Habitats) Regulations (Northern Ireland) 1995 (as amended)	The Department of the Environment designates SACs and SPAs in accordance with these Regulations. Under this legislation it is an offence to carry out any operation likely to damage a SAC or SPA without permission from the NIEA.	Northern Ireland

Legislation	Key requirements	Applicable Nation(s)
The Wildlife (Northern Ireland) Order, 1985 (as amended)	Makes it an offence to intentionally kill, injure, or take any wild bird or their eggs or nests. The Order also prohibits certain methods of recklessly killing, injuring, or taking birds, restricts the sale and possession of captive bred birds, and sets standards for keeping birds in captivity. Similar rules apply to wild animals. It also protects badgers and invasive species controls.	Northern Ireland
Noxious Weeds (Northern Ireland) Order, 1977	Requires the occupiers of land on which noxious weeds are growing to take action to prevent the spread of such weeds. The Act specifies such species as wild oat, thistle, dock and ragwort. For further information contact Department of Agriculture and Rural Development Northern Ireland (DARDNI).	Northern Ireland

4.2 THE HISTORIC ENVIRONMENT AND ARCHAEOLOGICAL REMAINS

4.2.1 Introduction

The historic environment is largely the visible historic landscape features, buildings and structures (**Figure 4.19**) that make up the unique character of each site or location. As well as physical elements, it can include places associated with important events, people, and social and technological developments in the past. Archaeological remains are part of the historic environment, but are often invisible, hidden from view and below ground.

Figure 4.19   *A 19th century pottery kiln found on a brownfield site (courtesy MoLA)*

4.2.2 Why is it important?

When planning for construction, if within the planning permission or client works information there are requirements (or conditions) relating to archaeology or the historic environment, it is because the site does, or has the potential to, contain a valuable and irreplaceable resource. This resource is potentially hugely diverse and represents the surviving evidence of a common cultural heritage, spanning the whole period of human history. The following may be equally significant depending on the context:

• study of ancient environments and the plants and animals that provided the basis for very early human occupation tens of thousands of years ago

- increasingly complex prehistoric societies that are known about only through archaeological record
- historic sites that complement documentary sources by providing a unique insight into developments in social organisation
- international relations and technology.

Historic Environment Local Management (HELM)

Provides information, training and guidance to decision makers whose actions affect the historic environment. All the latest guidance papers, good practice case studies, and latest information on planning and legislative changes can be accessed including specific and up to date guidance on historic buildings, landscapes and archaeological methods.

Go to: **www.helm.org.uk**

Cadw

Provides advice on all legislation, policy, guidance, protection and conservation issues specific to Wales for the historic environment and archaeology.

Go to: **www.cadw.wales.gov.uk/historicenvironment**

Historic Scotland

Provides advice on all legislation, policy, guidance, protection and conservation issues specific to Scotland for the historic environment and archaeology.

Go to: **www.historic-scotland.gov.uk**

NIEA

Provides advice on all legislation, policy, guidance, protection and conservation issues specific to Northern Ireland for the historic environment and archaeology.

Go to: **www.doeni.gov.uk/niea**

4.2.3 What is the objective?

The objective is the preservation and conservation of historic places and gain new knowledge from the investigation of archaeological sites.

A positive and proactive approach to the historic environment and archaeology on the site will allow two things to be achieved. Firstly, to effectively control the programme and cost risk that can accompany these types of constraints. Secondly, to be able to contribute to important social and scientific research that is ultimately undertaken for the wider public benefit. This can in turn provide organisations with the opportunity to progress their sustainability and social responsibility objectives.

Keep in mind the following:

- work collaboratively and take advice from a professional archaeologist
- plan ahead and arrange regular team reviews to identify and manage risks
- apply for in particular archaeological investigations, as soon as reasonably possible in the programme
- achieve maximum benefits for the organisation through open communication with the public
- the checklists within this guide (see **Section 4.2.8**).

4.2.4 Pre-construction review

Thoroughly review all planning conditions and consents relating to the historic environment and archaeology and ask the following questions:

1   What is the scope of historic environment recording works required in the pre-construction or enabling works phase and main phase?

2   What duties are there in respect of the historic environment and what are the risks?

3   How can the required work be completed as early as possible?

4   Are historic building surveys, baseline settlement monitoring, or removal/relocation or other protection works required for historic structures?

5   Is a pre-construction archaeological investigation (or archaeological evaluation) required (eg trial pits or other intrusive type surveys)? This may be usefully integrated with other essential site surveys for geotechnical or contamination investigations.

6   Who will undertake the work? Specialist historic surveys or archaeological investigations should be undertaken by a suitably qualified individual or organisation (Barber *et al*, 2008).

7   Has sufficient programme time and costs been allowed for specialist surveys, health and safety plans, list of required attendances and temporary works?

8   Have MS contents been provided by prospective specialist suppliers and fully integrated with enabling works programmes?

9   Have any access constraints (such as ownership, land use or seasonal survey issues) been addressed?

Documentation checklist

- **Approved desk study:** prepared to inform the project design and planning application. It may be a separate report or incorporated in the Written Scheme of Investigation (WSI) and provides invaluable background to the significance of the historic environment at the site – read it and use it.
- **WSI:** usually prepared by the specialist contractor/design archaeologist and should set out as a minimum, the scope, specification and outline programme for surveys and larger investigations together with procedures for dealing with unexpected or extensive discoveries.

- **Archaeological excavation MS:** include as a minimum the resources, temporary works, equipment, attendances required, safe working methods, working hours, communication plan and any proposals for public engagement.

- **Legal consents:** scheduled monument consent (SMC), listed building consent, exhumation licence etc as appropriate.

- **Notice:** provided to relevant regulator (local authority or national heritage agency as appropriate) concerning the start of works.

- **Post-excavation MS:** to include proposals for completion of off-site works and deposition of reports and finds with a local museum or other archive depositary and wider dissemination of the discoveries made.

4.2.5 Achieving good practice on site

Competent person

Ensure that a competent person is appointed to oversee and manage the historic environment and archaeological aspects of the project. This should ideally be an archaeologist or historic buildings specialist, independent of archaeological contractors or regulators involved in the project. On smaller projects the environmental manager or general site manager may undertake the role and should be tasked with liaising with specialists and regulators.

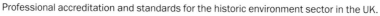

The Chartered Institute for Archaeologists (CIfA)

Professional accreditation and standards for the historic environment sector in the UK.

Go to: **www.archaeologists.net**

Institute of Archaeologists of Ireland (IAI)

Professional accreditation and standards for the historic environment sector in Eire and Northern Ireland.

Go to: **www.iai.ie**

Institute of Historic Building Conservation (IHBC)

Principal professional body for building conservation practitioners and historic environment specialists.

Go to: **www.ihbc.org.uk**

Documentation

Ensure that historic environment and archaeology requirements (that could include excavation, recording or monitoring for settlement, vibration and groundwater levels) are clearly set out in the EMP and included in site inductions and regular toolbox talks to both site-based management teams and site teams.

Trial pits and excavations for archaeology need to follow construction site good practice and any planned activities should be clearly set out in the EMP and detailed in the WSI. The WSI should clearly set out the scope, specification, and timing of the work including attendances, plant and equipment needed for the works and any constraints on the contractors methods, such as use of flat bladed buckets for excavation.

Periods for surveys and investigation of historic structures and archaeological remains should be clearly identified in the construction programme.

Ensure that drawings issued for construction clearly identify areas and features that need protection during the works, and areas that are subject to monitoring and supervision. Also ensure works by archaeological specialists and that the order and sequence of archaeological investigation is integrated with proposed site construction sequence. This is best achieved and checked through collaborative pre-start meetings.

Site plans should record the *in situ* archaeology identified that will be retained or removed. Plans for monitoring archaeology being retained should be put in place and reviewed during the project.

Weekly/progress meeting

Short notice changes to construction designs arising from ground conditions for example, can affect the scope or specification of archaeological works or required consents. Early warning of these at the weekly and/or progress meetings helps ensure that change can be accommodated with least disruption.

Site management

Archaeological works (**Figure 4.20**) need to follow the EMP and site best practise (see *Documentation*). Site inductions and regular toolbox talks to both archaeology and site teams should be undertaken.

Signage and demarcation of areas subject to protection or investigation should be used to inform site operatives of constraints and avoid inadvertent damage to historic assets and archaeological remains on site.

The requirement for an archaeologist to monitor another contractor's works (known as an archaeological watching brief) together with the name and contact telephone number of the

Figure 4.20   Archaeological excavation (courtesy Skanska)

archaeological contractor should be included on pre-start checklists and daily briefings or permits to dig. Permits to demolish structures should not be issued until required historic building survey reports are received and authorised by the project manager or client.

Liaison and communication from site managers to archaeology works is important to establish timing of works and follow site safety protocols.

Once recording and investigations are underway on site, the competent person has a duty to perform the works in a tidy and in a professional manner. Soil management and the maintaining of a safe and secure work area should be monitored by the competent person. Segregation from other activities should be maintained with appropriate temporary barriers. Safe access and walkways should be provided (such as Youngman's boards). Cover form the elements is essential if, for example, excavating human remains, or advisable, for example to ensure that the programme is maintained. Adequate lighting should be provided to ensure that survey and photographic standards are met.

The competent person should expect that contracted archaeological staff follow the site rules, comply with site working hours and provide a high quality and professional service to the project. Quality, safety or behavioural issues should be referred to the management of the archaeological company or relevant professional institute.

Unexpected discoveries

Major discoveries (Figure 4.21), unanticipated at the planning stage of a project do occur, but rarely. Depending on the level of risk a contingency sum and programme period may have been built into the project. In any event the most important action will be early and comprehensive communication with the client, the regulator and the project management and teams.

Courses of action will comprise either full excavation, or preservation *in situ* of the remains or a combination.

Treasure

In England, Wales and Northern Ireland, finds of precious metal are reportable to the relevant registrar at the Coroner's Office within 14 days. There are different

Figure 4.21   *The unexpected discovery of human remains can cause delays (courtesy Skanska)*

categories of find (Figure 4.22), and specific advice according to the jurisdiction is published by the relevant government department.

In Scotland all finds should be reported as soon as possible to the Treasure Trove Unit. All finds of precious metal should be reported to the project manager or competent person immediately and the

Carry out appropriate surveys to reduce the risk of unexpected discoveries.

archaeologist called to inspect the find to determine whether it is in association with other important objects.

Figure 4.22   Archaeological artefacts
(courtesy Skanska)

If suspected precious metals are discovered work should cease immediately. The object should be kept in a secure place and the finder's and the landowner's names and addresses and the time and place of discovery should be recorded in writing for submission to the local coroner. This will ensure that the finder's and landowner's interest is considered, when any reward may be determined.

Human remains

Legislation concerning the disturbance of buried human remains (**Figure 4.23**) varies across the UK. A licence may be required before site works start and the terms of any conditions and licences are complex, so specialist advice is essential if it is at all likely that burials will be encountered.

If suspected human remains are found unexpectedly on site – stop work and cover the excavation from public view. Contact an archaeologist immediately to determine if they are human or animal. If they are human remains a licence will be required from the Ministry of Justice. This can usually be obtained within 24 hours from reporting the find. Conditions may allow for the work to continue, but only under the supervision of the archaeologist. In Northern Ireland the Police (PSNI) and the Coroner's Office must be contacted when human remains are uncovered. In Scotland, it is the developers' responsibility to inform the police immediately on the discovery of any human remains.

Buildings of special architectural or historic interest

Many buildings, other structures and areas are 'listed'. In the UK this means that they are protected by law. Measures to protect and/or record these structures should have been identified at the planning stage of the project and included in the EMP and/or MS.

Many other buildings or structures may be on a local authority register of important historic buildings or may not be currently recognised as important historic structures. Before demolition orders being implemented on known structures or if historic structures are discovered during ground clearance, the following checks should be made to ensure that there is no loss of important historic fabric without record:

- obtain the opinion of the professional buildings archaeologists to determine significance

- complete a photographic and built structural record of the structure if the assets are of historic interest. This may be completed quickly at little cost and the results should be submitted to the relevant local archives

- if in doubt, contact the local authority conservation office.

Sustainable reuse of historic materials

Where possible do consider the option to reuse historic features, fabric and materials either within the project or by a third party organisation (subject to agreement with the competent person and the archaeological contractor).

Figure 4.23 Archaeological excavation of human remains (courtesy MoLA)

Preservation *in situ*

Where archaeological remains may be retained and preserved *in situ* care should be taken to ensure that published methods are followed and where necessary, specialist advice is obtained. For sources and advice contact the relevant regulator.

Visitors and monitoring

Dependent on the regulatory framework, site works for the historic environment may require monitoring by external officers based with a local or national authority. Other external visitors may include specialists based with museums or university departments. Ensure that these visits are planned in advance, are timed to provide the maximum benefit and that the client and or main contractor are properly represented. Advice or instruction received from external organisations should be formerly documented. Changes to the accepted scope and programme of works should not be implemented without the project manager's approval.

Public interest and the media

Opportunities to engage with the public and media and to display finds (both temporarily and built into permanent works) are encouraged as part of the sustainability agenda for the historic environment. The justification is that ultimately these belong to everyone, and that there is a genuine opportunity to create public benefit, particularly for local communities. Projects have a responsibility to fulfil these aims where justified by the level of potential interest.

Completion certificates

These forms record the period of time taken for specific activities and the date and time that areas are handed back for construction. They should be issued by the archaeologist and be countersigned by the relevant construction site manager, so that documentation exists to quantify the impact of archaeological works.

> All archives arising from surveys undertaken on site should be deposited with the appropriate local museum as soon as reasonably practicable. In Scotland this is via the Royal Commission on the Ancient and Historical Monuments of Scotland and artefacts via the Treasure Trove Unit.

4.2.6 Off-site works

It is often said that person hours on site for an archaeological investigation are matched 1:1 by the resources needed in laboratory work to bring the finds and data collected to a conclusion.

Scientific studies of the environmental and artefact assemblages and the formal publication of the results may take a considerable time to complete.

Reports and deposition of archives, for the results of historic building recording and archaeological surveys and excavations not requiring highly specialist external input, should be completed significantly quicker. A completion target for off-site works can be usefully set at 24 months from completion of the site work and should only rarely exceed that.

4.2.7 Completion and close out

On completion of the site work, the following should be taken into account.

Conditions and undertakings

Planning conditions will often not be fully discharged until all off-site works are completed. The site team should ensure that the competent person transfers the duty of supervision to another competent person in order to maintain momentum on site for a successful and timely conclusion to the project.

Consents

Please check the conditions set against consents to ensure that the deposition of documents, publications and archives relating to designated sites is successfully closed out.

Licences

Conditions attached to an exhumation license of human remains may require reburial of remains by a certain date. Ensure that this is achieved, or transfer that duty to a supplier, before closing out the project. In Northern Ireland the archaeological excavation licence granted by NIEA will have specific conditions attached that must be satisfied for it to be legally closed out.

Ownership of finds

Excepting finds falling under legislation for treasure that has a separate process, the artefacts discovered on a construction site will belong to the landowner or to the Crown in Scotland. In most cases finds should be deposited with the local museum who should have been contacted at the project start by the archaeological contractor or competent person. This situation will vary according to which UK jurisdiction the project is located in and specific advice should be sought.

4.2.8 Good practice checklists

Pre-construction	
Consents and licenses identified and approved	
Required historic building and archaeology surveys identified	
Specialist suppliers procured (eg archaeological contractor, historic buildings specialist)	
Historic environment surveys fully integrated with programme	
Pre-construction documentation in place (see Section 4.2.4)	
Agreed procedure to handle unexpected discoveries in place	
Toolbox talk prepared	

Construction	
Competent person appointed (see Section 4.2.5)	
Historic environment issues covered in EMP and/or MS	

Construction	✓
Historic environment issues identified on Issued for Construction (IFC) drawings	
Construction programmes up to date with historic environment surveys	
Communication plan and weekly (or other period) meetings arranged	
Signage and demarcation of sensitive areas on site	
Archaeologist's contact details added to daily briefings and permit system	
Site audit – works are continuing in safe and tidy manner	
Appropriate attendances in place (eg plant, operatives, lighting, welfare)	
Potential for reuse of historic materials reviewed and actioned	

Off site	✓
Instructions for reporting and post-excavation analysis issued	
Delivery programme agreed	

Completion and close out	✓
Planning conditions discharged	
Consent conditions closed out	
License conditions closed out	
Finds ownership transfer deeds issued	
Publications released and reports submitted to relevant historic environment record	
All archives submitted to public depository	

4.2.9   Legislation

Legislation is constantly changing, including amendments and new legislation, and this varies between England, Wales, Scotland and Northern Ireland. If site staff are unsure on any environmental issue, contact the regional environmental regulator for advice.

Legislation	Key requirements	Applicable Nation(s)
Planning (Listed Buildings and Conservation Areas) (Scotland) Act, 1997	Any works involving the demolition, alteration, or extension, of a listed building that would affect its character as a listed building requires consent from Historic Scotland. Local authorities can also designate as conservation areas any area of special architectural or historic interest, the character or appearance of which is desirable to preserve or enhance. Most local authorities will provide supplementary planning guidance for such areas.	Scotland
Planning (Listed Buildings and Conservation Areas) Act, 1990 (as amended)	Any works involving the demolition, alteration, or extension, of a listed building that would affect its character as a listed building requires consent from Historic England, Cadw, NIEA. Local authorities/DOENI can designate as conservation areas any area of special architectural or historic interest, the character or appearance of which is desirable to preserve or enhance. Most local authorities/DOENI will provide supplementary planning guidance for such areas.	England, Wales, Northern Ireland
Ancient Monuments and Archaeological Areas Act 1979	Scheduled monument consent is required for any works involving "demolishing, destroying, removing, repairing, altering, adding to, flooding or tipping material onto the monument or around it".	England, Wales, Scotland, Northern Ireland
Burials Act 1857 and Disused Burial Grounds Act 1981 (as amended)	Under the Burials Act 1857 it is necessary to obtain a license from the Home Office to disturb any burials. The Disused Burial Grounds Act 1981 sets stringent conditions regarding the removal and disposal of human remains.	England, Wales, Northern Ireland

4.3   LAND CONTAMINATION

4.3.1   Introduction

Land contamination can be caused by previous land use, criminal activity such as fly-tipping or naturally occurring substances in the land, for example naturally occurring radioactive material (NORM) or arsenic.

However, all land has background levels of substances that vary depending on factors such as geographical location and geology. The presence of contamination does not necessarily mean that there is a need or a legal liability to clean-up. The existence of contamination (**Figure 4.24**) can be entirely consistent with the current

Figure 4.24   Chromium contaminated land (courtesy SEPA)

use of the land if it is not causing any unacceptable risk. However, if there are proposals for redevelopment, then land contaminated may require remediation, so that the land is suitable for its intended use (Ander *et al*, 2011).

This section advises on how to assess and manage risks due to land contamination, how to avoid causing or spreading contamination and outlines procedures to manage special contaminants such as unexploded ordnance (see Section 4.3.6).

4.3.2 Why is managing contaminated land important?

For contamination to cause an impact on a receptor there needs to be a means of reaching that receptor.

Construction activities physically affect land that may create pathways by which contaminants can reach receptors and cause risks to:

- site-based staff (through contact with soils or inhalation of dust or gases)
- ecological systems
- buildings and structures
- ground and surface waters
- users of the land through contact with soil or via food grown on the land.

Land contamination may also give rise to leachates (liquids containing dissolved contaminants) that can also pollute ground and surface water.

Key legislative controls

The principles of regulation involve:

- stopping new contaminated land being created and in the event of an incident:
  - ○ that the effect of the contaminant(s) is fully remediated
  - ○ any damage caused is compensated until remediation is achieved
- taking a risk-based approach to tackling historical contamination.

Planning

In the UK, land contamination and remediation is a material consideration within the planning regime. Planning authorities consider the potential implications of contamination, both when developing structural or local plans and when considering applications for planning consent, which may result in a requirement for remediation to be undertaken.

Statutory contaminated land

In addition to controls via the planning system, there is legislation that applies (in the UK and Ireland) to land that has been contaminated historically. Alongside statutory guidance this has created a regime for the identification and remediation of contaminated land.

Environmental damage

Where there is imminent risk of environmental damage occurring to land, surface water or habitats steps need to be taken to prevent such damage or to address it if the problem has already started to occur. Legislation sets out roles and responsibilities for preventing or remedying damage including compensation for the cumulative impact the damage has had until it is remediated.

Figure 4.25   *Soil testing being undertaken (courtesy Parsons Brinckerhoff)*

Impacts of land contamination on construction

Land contamination may result in the following problems:

- delays to construction programmes through unexpected or accidental contamination (spills and leaks)
- liability for costs for making contamination worse, resulting from activities on site or from inappropriate management and/or remediation of contamination
- blight and subsequent reduction of the site value
- pollution of groundwater and surface watercourses
- effects on flora or fauna
- public concern, anxiety and ill health.

4.3.3   Responsibilities to assess and remediate land

In general terms when buying land, the principle of caveat emptor (buyer beware) applies because the seller has more information about what they are selling than buyers do. In terms of land contamination, not all potentially contaminated land shows up on a land survey, so often buyers ask for land condition assessments (**Figure 4.25**) when acquiring land. This helps determine what follow up assessment and action may be needed to clean up the land, so that the planned development can be constructed.

Under the planning system, where land is affected by contamination issues, responsibility for safe development rests with the developer.

Under UK legislation the polluter pays principle (PPP) is applied in two ways:

1   Where possible the costs of remediating pollution should be borne by the polluter. However, sometimes the polluter cannot be found, and then the responsibility for contamination may fall to the land owner or occupier. This is particularly the case when land has been sold on under the principle of **caveat emptor**.

2   When an incident has occurred that adversely affects the integrity of a SSSI, conservation status of species or habitats protected by legislation outside SSSIs, surface or groundwater that changes the water's status and/or human health. It places responsibility on the site operator to take immediate steps to remedy damage to land. There are grounds for appeal, complementary and compensatory action.

4.3.4   How to avoid problems – adequate assessment and management of risk

Problems are best avoided and/or managed by gaining as full an understanding of the site as possible before works start. A vigorous process of identifying and evaluating risk is undertaken to decide appropriate means by which risks may be reduced to acceptable levels or eliminated. Remedial works are normally only required for land where unacceptable risks are clearly identified. The EA/Defra (2004) model procedures identify several phases of this risk assessment process and provide guidance on the development of a remediation strategy that should be agreed by the LPA and other parties before any work begins.

All sites where contaminated land is suspected need to be assessed to at least the first tier of risk assessment (see **Section 3.2.4**) before construction work starts. This will help to minimise risks to site staff and allow site procedures to incorporate measures to reduce the spread of contamination.

When a contaminant has been identified on site, it does not necessarily mean there is a risk. For example, where there is a contaminant present, but there is no pathway by which it could come into contact with a receptor, the contaminant-pathway-receptor linkage is not complete, so the land in its present state poses minimal risk to the receptor.

However, construction activities can mobilise contaminants (for example, the excavation of soil that brings contamination to the surface, and the installation of drains may create a conduit along which contaminants mobilised by rainwater, may travel), so that they may reach the receptor.

So, a site is only considered to pose a risk if there is at least one valid contaminant-pathway-receptor linkage, called a pollutant linkage (**Figure 3.4**).

Avoid spreading contamination during construction

Many activities on site could lead to spreading of the contaminants that may create a pathway to the receptor. These include:

- wind-blown contaminated dust arising from loading of lorries or stockpiled contaminated material on clean ground during works
- spillages of contaminants such as oil or chemicals onto the ground during works
- dewatering of excavations that draws in contaminated groundwater from nearby sites
- release of volatile vapours
- discharge of contaminated water into nearby watercourses (eg by site dewatering)
- infiltration of rainwater on uncovered stockpiles results in contaminated runoff or leaching of contaminants into clean ground.

Site procedures should take account of risks that can cause contamination and should include measure to prevent or minimise those risks. Emergency plans should confirm actions to be taken if contamination is found to have arisen and site operatives appropriately trained and competent to reduce incident response times and consequential impacts.

What to do if unexpected contamination is encountered

Although a robust site characterisation should reduce the likelihood of discovering unexpected contamination during site works, unearthing unexpected contamination is always possible (**Figure 4.26**).

Contractors should always be encouraged to make contingency plans for managing unexpected findings and MSs should always identify the possibility that contamination might be found and outline the mechanisms for dealing with this. Site-based staff (especially excavator operators and drilling contractors) should be vigilant during excavations and earthworks (see *Visual signs* checklist at the end of the section).

Figure 4.26   Discovery of contaminated land (coiurtesy BAM Nuttall)

During boring, digging, excavating and similar operations, the relevant operators should observe the uncovered ground and watch out for visual signs of contamination, for example unusual colouring or ground structure. Operatives should also be made aware that the release of noxious fumes, petrol, oils, solvents, chemical residues and smells may indicate contamination and must be acted upon.

It is good practice to create a 'quarantine' area on sites where contamination may be encountered. This area should be hard surfaced to control fugitive leachates, fenced to minimise contact and away from site buildings, site traffic and neighbouring properties.

When contamination is suspected, the following procedures should be adopted:

1   Stop work immediately.

2   Report the discovery to the site manager, so they can consult an expert for advice.

3   Isolate the area and contain any spread of contaminants.

4   Clear the affected area of the site leaving nothing that could be a source of ignition.

5   Contact the appropriate regulator if it suspected or likely that contamination has been found.

6   Ensure that the suspected contamination is tested and characterised and agree changes to any existing remedial plan or produce a remedial plan if none exists.

Special measures may be needed where the contaminated discovered presents a particular acute risk, such as unexploded ordnance (UXO) (see Section 4.3.6).

4.3.5   Remediating contaminated land including verification

If measures to manage contamination are necessary a remediation strategy needs to be developed, implemented and verified to demonstrate the strategy has been successfully completed (Figure 4.27). The remediation framework for land affected by contamination is outlined in EA/ Defra (2004) and Rudland and Jackson (2004).

Figure 4.27   Land remediation (courtesy Parsons Brinckerhoff)

Available contaminated land remediation approaches

There are a wide range of remediation techniques that have been applied in the UK (**Figure 4.28**). These may involve one or more approaches applied sequentially or in parallel. They may treat the contamination in order that it might be:

● contained or immobilised

● separated to recover materials that can be reused

● destroyed.

Many of these require an appropriate environmental permit or exemption in place from the local authority or environmental regulator before starting treatment.

These options should be considered on a site-by-site basis and careful evaluation of the options will be part of the remediation strategy.

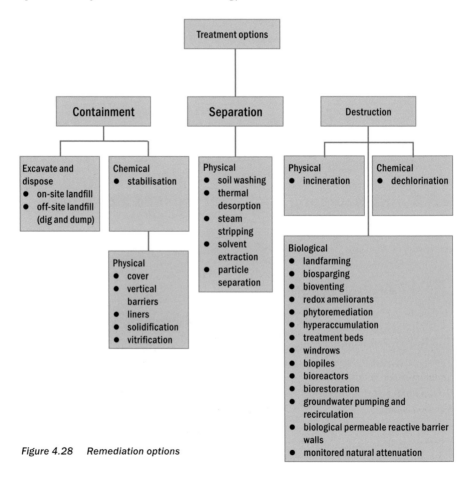

Figure 4.28   Remediation options

4.3.6   Unexploded ordnance – a special contaminant

The discovery of UXO during construction works is unusual, and is only likely to occur in areas of historic weapons manufacture or storage during the world wars. However, they may be discovered in areas that received heavy bombardment during the Second World War, particularly urban areas such as London, Liverpool and Coventry and pose a threat of significant damage to the environment and the public if not managed properly.

In practical terms, the risk from UXO is greatest for contractor's employees undertaking the works on site. However all parties involved in the design, management and planning of a construction project have statutory duties in reducing the risk.

The different stages that should be applied in UXO risk assessment are:

1   Preliminary risk assessment.

2   Detailed risk assessment.

3   Risk mitigation.

4   Implementation.

Note that the remediation options summarised in **Figure 4.28** are not appropriate for UXO. The principal procedures of mitigating UXO risk are:

● review and revise development plan

● UXO detection survey

● UXO target investigation

● UXO classification

● site clearance.

4.3.7   Good practice checklists

Get to know the site and remedial plans	
Review/carry out a preliminary investigation of site using the approach set out in EA/Defra (2004) to develop the conceptual site model (CSM)	
If the CSM indicates that there are potential contaminant-pathway-receptor linkages, undertake exploratory investigations of the site to characterise contamination in terms of: ● nature ● concentration ● extent and location	
Refine the CSM by collecting further information and assess whether the contaminant will cause or potentially cause significant harm to a receptor	

Get to know the site and remedial plans	✓
Refine the CSM if areas of contamination are being left to naturally attenuate as the construction works take place and amendments are made to plans as these may create new contaminant-pathway-receptor linkage	
Develop a remediation strategy including plans for verification and ongoing monitoring	
Agree the remediation strategy with the local authority or environmental regulator and make it (and the supporting assessment information) available to the contractor	
Obtain relevant permits for any remedial works required	

Avoid causing or spreading contamination	✓
Avoid stockpiling contaminated soil unless it cannot be avoided. If it is necessary, stockpile only on a hard-standing area to prevent contamination of underlying ground	
Cover stockpiled material to prevent wind-blown (potentially contaminated) dust and to prevent ingress of rainwater	
Control surface water drainage from stockpiled area. Water draining from a stockpile may be contaminated and require controlled off-site disposal	
Take care when handling, storing and using oils and chemicals	
Identify a quarantine area for particularly hazardous materials	

Remaining vigilant during construction	✓
Look for visual signs of contamination	
Discoloured soil (eg chemical residues)	
Unexpected odours (eg hydrocarbons such as petrol)	
Fibrous texture to the soil (eg asbestos)	
Presence of foreign objects (eg chemical/oil containers/waste)	
Evidence of previous soil workings	
Evidence of underground or above ground storage infrastructure such as fuel tanks and dispensers	
Existence of waste pits and infilled ground	
Artificial ground where the level has been raised by past activities and not due to natural causes (a common example is construction platforms for old industrial buildings made of imported industrial wastes such as ash)	
Old drain runs and contamination within buildings such as tanks, flues etc	
Seepage of leachates and liquors from fissures etc indicating a hidden source	

Remaining vigilant during construction	✓
Presence of contaminated soakaways and unlined voids (such as tar wells on some old gas-producing sites)	
Report suspected contamination so that it can be investigated by a competent person	
Update records with any new findings so risk can be managed	

4.3.8 Further reading

ENVIRONMENT AGENCY (2010a) *Guiding principles for land contamination 1*, GPLC1, Environment Agency, Bristol. Go to: **http://tinyurl.com/o4m3oru**

STONE, K, MURRAY, A, COOKE, S, FORAN, J and GOODERHAM, L (2009) *Unexploded ordnance (UXO) A guide for the construction industry*, C681, CIRIA, London (ISBN: 978-0-86017-681-7). Go to: **www.ciria.org**

BS 10175:2011+A1:2013 *Investigation of potentially contaminated sites – code of practice*

4.3.9 Legislation

Legislation is constantly changing, including amendments and new legislation, and this varies between England, Wales, Scotland and Northern Ireland. If site staff are unsure on any environmental issue, contact the regional environmental regulator for advice.

Legislation	Key requirements	Applicable Nation(s)
Environmental Protection Act 1990 (as amended)	It requires that local authorities identify contaminated land and ensure that significant risks are dealt with. It also establishes rules for who should pay for remediation.	England, Wales, Scotland, Northern Ireland
Town and Country Planning Act 1990	Local planning authorities are responsible for ensuring that land contamination is dealt with through the planning system and that remediation takes place where it is required. It is the responsibility of the developer to carry out the remediation and satisfy the local authority that the remediation has been carried out as agreed.	England, Wales
The Environmental Damage (Prevention and Remediation) Regulations 2009 Environmental Damage (Prevention and Remediation) (Wales) Regulations 2009	If a business carries out an activity that causes environmental damage they will have to remedy the damage. If there is a risk of damage from any business activities, the damage must be prevented. Overall, the Regulations are likely to be used only for the most serious cases of damage.	England, Wales, Scotland, Northern Ireland

Legislation	Key requirements	Applicable Nation(s)
Environmental Liability (Scotland) Regulations 2009 (as amended) Environmental Liability (Prevention and Remediation) Regulations (Northern Ireland) 2009 (as amended)	Under the Regulations, environmental damage is: • damage to surface or groundwater such that its classification is affected • contamination of land where there is a significant risk to human health • damage to EU protected natural habitats and species or damage to SSSIs/ASSIs.	England, Wales, Scotland, Northern Ireland
Contaminated Land (England) Regulations 2006 (as amended) Contaminated Land (Wales) Regulations 2006 (as amended) Contaminated Land (Scotland) Regulations 2005	Further define land contamination and special sites also explains the rules for how appeals can be made against decisions taken under the Environmental Protection Act 1990 (as amended).	England, Wales, Scotland
The Control of Substances Hazardous to Health (COSHH) Regulations 2002 (as amended) Control of Substances Hazardous to Health Regulations (Northern Ireland) 2003 (as amended)	The regulation requires employers to carry out a risk assessments and as a result, take steps to either prevent exposure or control the risks to their employees (and others who may be affected) from such substances.	England, Wales, Scotland, Northern Ireland
Waste and Contaminated Land (Northern Ireland) Order 1997 (as amended) Waste and Contaminated Land (Amendment) Act (Northern Ireland) 2011	Sets out the waste management regime covering waste carrier registration and identifying and remedying contaminated land. Changes the legislative framework for management of land that has been contaminated by pollution. Gives the DOE and district councils similar investigative, enforcement and clean up powers to deal with illegally dumped waste.	Northern Ireland

4.4 NUISANCE

4.4.1 Dust, emissions and odours

4.4.1.1 Introduction

Dust is considered to be any airborne particulate matter up to 75 µm in diameter. In addition to causing a nuisance to neighbouring properties and vehicles, dust may lead to several health issues including eye, nose and throat irritation as well as exposure to respirable dust exacerbating pre-existing medical conditions such as chronic obstructive pulmonary disease (COPD) and asthma. Also, dust may cause adverse ecological impacts to both aquatic and non-aquatic plants and animals.

Emissions from plant and generators may cause air pollution and odours. These smaller particles may be inhaled leading to respiratory problems and long-term cardiovascular health issues. Odours associated with waste organic material, sewage or from chemicals can cause nuisance.

Where the local authority considers that a statutory nuisance is occurring then an abatement notice must be served. This may have cost, programme and reputational implications for the project team. Legal claims and civil compensation may also arise for expenses, for example associated with car washing and window cleaning or damage to crops in rural areas.

Common sources of dust, emissions and odours are:

- dry, unpaved haul roads
- mud on public roads
- tipping (from height)
- uncovered vehicle movements
- uncontained/uncovered equipment (eg crushers, conveyors)
- material stockpiles
- cutting, grinding and drilling operations
- shot-blasting
- earthworks.

4.4.1.2 Why is the management of dust, emissions and odours important?

Dust, emissions and odours arising from a site can cause health risks to site-based staff and neighbours, air pollution, and annoyance to local residents.

Legal action, under either criminal or common law is possible and could result in delays, costs, instructions to cease activity and damage to reputation.

Dust particle sizes can vary considerably, depending on their origin, and the smallest particles can be inhaled. Some dust, such as limestone, is chemically active and inert dusts such as silica are associated with lung disease. Emissions from plant and generators can pollute the atmosphere, and can create unpleasant odours as well as potentially being hazardous to health from PM10 and 2.5 from combustion sources.

Neighbours

Annoyance is caused when residents have to re-clean washing and when they have to wash cars, curtains and windows. Wind-blown dust can be unsightly over long distances in scenic areas. Dust commonly causes eye irritation, but the more exceptional effect would be in exacerbating pre-existing health conditions (eg COPD, asthma).

Dust impacts on crops and ecology

Claims are particularly common on rural road projects. Even very low concentrations of dust can affect plant and fruit growth. Plant growth is especially susceptible to dusts that are highly alkaline (eg cement dust). Claims for damage to crops in excess of half a mile from the site have been made because dust can be blown for long distances. Dust blowing onto watercourses can damage the ecology. Ash trees may drop their leaves up to eight weeks early following exposure to high levels of dust.

> The managing director of a developer was fined more than £18 000 after the company started green vegetation bonfires at a residential development in breach of a previously issued abatement notice.

Impact on project programme and budget

Some contracts may specify that no work occurs at times of high wind in a certain direction. Working to comply with strict dust levels can impose cost and/or programme constraints. If a statutory nuisance is occurring an abatement notice will be served by the local authority.

4.4.1.3 Legal requirements

Local authorities are required to inspect their areas and investigate any complaints made relating to dust, emissions and odour nuisance under the Local Authority Pollution Control (LAPC) regime.

Statutory nuisances or breaches of permits issued by a local authority to control activities causing emissions to air (eg mobile crusher activities carried out under a mobile part B permit) can result in abatement notices or enforcement action (in terms of breach of permit) being served when complaints have been received.

It is also important to note that statuary nuisance abatement notices will not be served where an environmental permit exists for the activity causing a nuisance, however enforcement action can be taken in the form of breach of permit. Potential nuisance issues such as noise, dust, odour and light control requirements will be detailed in the company environmental permit and must be complied with. An example of an activity that may cause dust and noise nuisance and may operate on a construction site under a permit would be a mobile concrete crusher. Mobile crushers must operate under a mobile part B permit.

To avoid causing complaints, the site should adopt good working practices:

- identify sensitive receptors and any activities likely to give rise to dust, odours or emissions affecting residential/surrounding land uses, schools, wildlife, statutory designations and watercourses

- in liaison with the local authority develop a dust management plan and adopt control measures to mitigate any negative effects (eg site speed limits, use of water bowsers, sheeting of vehicles and skips)

- undertake daily monitoring and keep a record of dust management activities and any complaints received

- undertake physical monitoring (eg glass slides, real time monitoring in sensitive areas)

- respond to monitoring results and any complaints received and notify the local authority of any actions taken.

4.4.1.4 How to avoid problems

Dust suppression

It is important to develop a strategy to stop dust being generated. Careful planning and design of construction operations can reduce dust for example:

- use of appropriate surfaces (ie tarmac) and speed limits on haul routes

- use of rumble strips at site egresses

- damping down of road surfaces

- wheel and vehicle washing

- road sweeping

- manual sweeping

- jet washing

- scraping to remove excess build-up of materials on site

> The monitoring regime should link into the management plan to trigger preventative measures and actions when monitoring results indicate elevated dust levels. Also, the regime should note weather conditions (including prevailing wind direction), construction activities, their location and duration on site. The dust control plan should employ best practicable means (BPM).

- haul vehicle covers

- locating enclosed stockpiles and batching plant in sheltered areas

- rolling and seeding stockpiles or covered (eg with jute matting)

- chemical binders applied to stockpiles or exposed ground

- water suppression and/or local extraction on cutting, grinding and drilling

- enclosing/covering equipment (eg crushers, conveyors)

- enclosing areas where shot-blasting is undertaken

- using sheeting/debris netting around scaffolding.

Damp down using water

Fine spraying of water (eg using a bowser, **Figure 4.29**) is the most effective way to suppress dust. Repeat spray regularly, especially during warm and sunny weather when water will evaporate quickly. However, ensure that the application does not create excessive mud or a flow of dirty water that can runoff into watercourses that could lead to prosecution by the environmental regulator. Consider spraying:

- unpaved work areas subject to traffic or wind

- site haul roads

- structures and buildings during demolition
- sand, spoil and aggregate stockpiles
- during the loading and unloading of dust generating materials.

Ideally, non-potable water should be used for damping down, eg rainwater captured on site or using water abstracted from a nearby watercourse.

Figure 4.29   Dust suppression (courtesy Galliford Try plc)

Note that if abstracting water for spraying from a watercourse or fire hydrant, a license is likely to be required, so ensure to obtain the appropriate consent (see **Section 4.7.6**). Also, consideration must be given as to where any discharges will go as a result of damping down dust (ie to storm drains or watercourses).

> When deciding on the techniques to be used to manage dust consider the source-pathway-receptor model (Figure 3.4).

Damp down using water with chemical additives or binders

Damping down, using water in dry weather only offers a temporary solution. For a longer lasting solution it may be appropriate to mix additives and chemical binders to the water. Spraying with water and chemical additives is more effective than using water alone because this will reduce the number of passes per day and the volume of water needed.

There are several additives on the market and the cost of the additives has to be considered against savings in water supply, bowser use, downtime and ecological risk. Take care to avoid over application that may cause pollution. Contact the environmental regulator for advice before using additives, especially if close to a watercourse or abstraction point.

Dust screening

If dust-generating activities cannot be avoided, it may help to erect screens to act as windbreaks or dust screens (**Figure 4.30**). These can take the form of permeable or semi-permeable fences, but they can be expensive if designed to resist high winds. Trees or shrubs planted early, as part of site landscaping, can provide some screening as can the retention of existing vegetation (or buildings to be demolished). Also, in building demolition, retention of external walls while internal demolition and deconstruction is being undertaken will offer dust screening.

Dust prediction and monitoring

There are several methods for monitoring dust on site, these include:

1. Carry out visual assessments of dust emissions from the various activities and also at the site boundary.

2. Exposing microscope slides or sticky pads for a given period to determine dust direction and deposition rate over the exposed period.

3. Using high volume samplers to draw air through a filter to measure the volume of dust in the air at the time of sampling.

4. Using a dry Frisbee dust deposit gauge (**Figure 4.31**) to collect large and small dust particles over one month intervals. The contents are then sent for analysis to determine deposition rates.

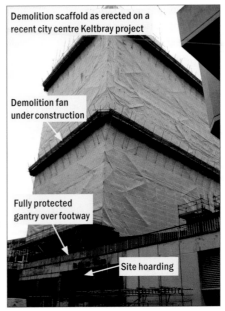

Figure 4.30   *Noise and dust mitigation (courtesy Brookfield Multiplex and Keltbray)*

For all methods used, samples need to be obtained before work starts to determine background levels for comparison against those taken during construction.

None of these methods provide definitive evidence of the effects of dust. If they are to be used to demonstrate commitment to good practice, then the cost needs to be accounted for in the long-term budget. It may be difficult to justify discontinuing monitoring once it has started. However, monitoring data may be useful evidence in defence of a nuisance claim.

For a dust monitoring programme to give more definitive evidence of the effects of construction it should include both upwind and downwind monitoring of the site and cover a baseline period before construction started (and after construction has been completed).

Monitoring ensures any potentially sensitive receptors are covered, eg schools. The baseline period should ideally cover the same seasons as the construction period.

Figure 4.31   *Dust monitoring (courtesy Balfour Beatty)*

As a minimum, carry out regular visual checks of dust across the site and at the site boundary, upwind and downwind. Keep a log of the results, which should also include details of the weather conditions at the time of the assessment (eg wind speed, direction).

Record and monitor complaints from members of the public and rectify substantiated complaints. Notify the local authority if appropriate. On large construction sites agree air quality action levels with the local authority and adopt a mitigation strategy if these levels are breached. This may require a range of dust monitoring techniques which could include real time monitoring Frisbee gauges and microscope slides in order to determine the deposition of dust and the level of dust soiling dependent on the sensitivity of the environment.

4.4.1.5 Emissions and odours

Processes involving the use of fuels and the heating and drying of materials commonly emit fumes, odours or smoke. It is important to prevent emissions and odours as far as possible (see checklist in **Section 4.4.1.6**).

Any works that risk creating odours should be planned appropriately so as to minimise any effect.

Any processes that emit fumes, odours or smoke should comply with the manufacturer's and if appropriate regulatory limits to prevent nuisance or a regulatory breach.

All plant and vehicles should comply with European Union (EU) emission limits for their vehicle class as a minimum and should be regularly maintained. A programme of maintenance checks should be developed for plant on site and adhered to.

Smoke from plant and fires could be deemed a statutory nuisance and/or the creation of dark smoke from an industrial or trade premise could be deemed an offence under the Clean Air Act 1993. The local authority can enforce (informally or formally) a stop to those activities generating the smoke.

If plant or machinery emits excessive (ie amounting to nuisance) levels of exhaust emissions, local authorities have the power to prescribe limits on those emissions, the breaching of which may be an offence. Old plant, or plant carrying out an operation it is not designed for, can be likely to fall foul of the prescribed limit.

Consider fitting exhaust filtration systems to vehicles. Ensure any plant and equipment emitting black smoke is taken out of service immediately and the defect rectified. As far as possible locate plant away from sensitive receptors, ie neighbours and local ecology. Where possible use mains or battery powered equipment over diesel powered.

4.4.1.6 Good practice checklists

Good housekeeping	✓
Haul routes	
Select suitable haul routes away from sensitive receptors if possible. Reduce the length and width of haul roads (while still allowing two-way traffic) to minimise the surface area that dust may be produced from	
Temporarily surface heavily used areas, or use geotextiles (eg around batching plant or haul routes)	
Carry out regular mechanical road sweeping, manual sweeping, scraping and jet washing to remove excess build-up of materials on site and public roads	
Limit vehicle speeds – the slower the vehicle the less dust generated	
Dampen down in dry weather	
Demolition	
Use enclosed conveyors and chutes for dropping demolition materials that have the potential to cause dust. Regularly dampen the chutes	
Obtain consent from the regulator for the use of mobile plant for crushing materials such as bricks, tiles and concrete. This permit will contain the explicit operating conditions for the site	
Use debris netting during demolition to reduce dust emissions	
Use water atomisers to reduce dust emissions	
Locate crushing plant away from sensitive receptors	
Deconstruct rather than demolish	
Plant and vehicles	
Ensure vehicles and plant used on site are well maintained and regularly serviced with full maintenance records	
Ensure that all vehicles used by contractors comply with MOT emissions standards at all times	
Any plant or vehicles emitting black smoke should be taken out of service immediately and defects rectified	
Clean the wheels and surfaces of vehicles leaving the site so that mud is not spread onto the highways	
Ensure that exhaust fumes are directed upwards and not directly at the ground	
Retractable sheeted covers on vehicles should be used to enclose dust	
Vehicles should keep to site speed limits to reduce the risk of dust clouds	
As far as possible locate plant away from sensitive receptors	
Control deliveries to site to minimise queuing	

Good housekeeping	✓
Make sure that engines are switched off when they are not in use	
Carry out refuelling in designated areas away from the public	

Materials handling and storage	
Locate stockpiles out of the wind (or provide wind breaks) to minimise the potential for dust generation	
Store materials away from the site boundary, main site access roads and downwind of sensitive receptors	
Keep the stockpiles to the minimum practicable height and use gentle slopes	
Site stockpiles within walled bays	
Damp down earthworks during dry weather	
Roll and re-vegetate long-term stockpiles, cover (eg using hessian or jute matting), and consider use of chemical dust suppressant additives for short-term control	
Minimise the height of fall of materials	
Ensure tipping of loads is carried out in a controlled manner	
Ensure all waste skips are enclosed or covered	

Concrete batching	
As far as possible store dry materials (eg cement) inside	
Mix large quantities of concrete or bentonite slurries in enclosed areas to avoid generating dust	
Cement should be stored in silos with appropriate dust abatement equipment	

Cutting/grinding/grouting/packing	
Minimise cutting and grinding on site where possible	
On cutters and saws, use equipment and techniques such as dust extractors to minimise dust. Consider a wet cutting saw or use vacuum extraction or block splitters	
Spray water during cutting of paving slabs to minimise dust	

Preventing emissions and odours	✓
Waste storage	
To avoid odours use covered containers for organic waste (eg food, weeds and other vegetation) and remove waste frequently	
Ensure that septic tanks are emptied regularly	
Chemicals on site	
Take account of the prevailing wind conditions when arranging activities that are likely to emit aerosols, fumes, odours and smoke	
Position site toilets away from residential areas	

4.4.1.7 Further reading

GLA (2006) *The control of dust and emissions from construction and demolition. Best practice guidance*, Greater London Authority, London (ISBN: 978-1-85261-942-8).
Go to: **http://tinyurl.com/p7k92ng**

HOLMAN, C (2014) *Guidance on the assessment of dust from demolition and construction*, Working Group of the Institute of Air Quality Management (IAQM), London.
Go to: **http://tinyurl.com/pbhc34u**

4.4.1.8 Legislation

Legislation is constantly changing, including amendments and new legislation, and this varies between England, Wales, Scotland and Northern Ireland. If site staff are unsure on any environmental issue contact the regional environmental regulator for advice.

Legislation	Key requirements	Applicable Nation(s)
Clean Neighbourhoods and Environment Act (Northern Ireland) 2011	Sets out rules on statutory nuisance, which could lead to the issuing of an abatement notice by the local authority	Northern Ireland
Clean Air Act 1993	It is an offence to permit the emission of dark smoke from industrial or trade premises, which is generally enforced by local authorities	England, Wales, Scotland
Environmental Protection Act 1990 (as amended)	Local authorities can serve an abatement notice upon the cause of a statutory nuisance to stop work immediately	England, Wales, Scotland
Clean Air (Northern Ireland) Order 1981	It is an offence to permit the emission of dark smoke from industrial or trade premises, which is generally enforced by local authorities	Northern Ireland

4.4.2 Lighting

4.4.2.1 Introduction

Adequate lighting on construction sites is required as part of occupational health and safety to allow safe working outside of daylight hours and also in areas restricted from natural light. However, lighting from construction projects can also cause light pollution.

Light itself is not a pollutant, but light pollution or nuisance is attributed to sources of light that have adverse effects on surrounding receptors. The most common source of light pollution from construction sites is temporary lighting spill into surrounding areas and/or disproportionate to the area requiring illumination. Other sources of light pollution from construction sites include security lighting, compounds and site offices.

4.4.2.2 Why is it important?

Light pollution arising from site can cause nuisance and annoyance to local residents and disturbance to local ecology. Local residents are most likely to be affected through light spillage onto buildings that disrupts natural sleep patterns. Prolonged disruption can lead to more serious health problems, such as stress.

Light spillage can also interfere with local ecology, such as birds and nocturnal species, in particular bats, amphibians and insects. The disturbance can affect migration, feeding and breeding patterns. Complaints from neighbours and disturbance to local ecology could result in delays, costs and damage to reputation.

There are also potential health risks, both for workers on site and members of the public, from lighting glare as this can cause impaired vision leading to accidents.

Excessive or inefficient lighting is also a waste of energy and indirectly brightens the night sky. The emergence of International Dark Sky Reserves certified by the International Dark-Sky Association (IDA) also means that there are additional protected areas to consider when installing lighting in parts of the UK.

> The mission of the International Dark-Sky Association (IDA) is to preserve and protect the night-time environment and our heritage of dark skies through environmentally responsible outdoor lighting.
>
> One of the IDA's objectives is to promote protection of nocturnal habitats, public enjoyment of the night sky and its heritage, and areas ideal for professional and /or amateur astronomy, which can be achieved through applying for a Dark Sky Reserve (DSR).
>
> A DSR is a public or private land of substantial size (of 700 km² or about 173 000 acres) possessing an exceptional or distinguished quality of starry nights and a nocturnal environment and that is specifically protected for its scientific, natural, educational, cultural heritage and/or public enjoyment.
>
> For more information go to: **www.darksky.org**

4.4.2.3 Lighting management

Controlling light pollution

Careful selection and planning of temporary lighting can reduce the effects of light pollution. This includes:

- identify sensitive receptors surrounding the site
- position/direct* lighting away from sensitive receptors
- use directional lighting
- use appropriate levels of illumination
- light areas only when and where required
- use the minimum amount of lighting, without compromising health and safety
- install hoods, louvers, shields, reflectors and baffles to mitigate or reduce light spillage.

To avoid unnecessary light pollution from site compounds and/or site offices and cabins, a 'switch off' scheme can be implemented. Training and posters can advise staff, including subcontractors, to turn off lighting when a room or area is not in use.

Alternatively, lighting could be controlled by motion sensors or a 'last man out' switch, whereby the last person can switch off all of the non-necessary lights in one single switch.

Where security lighting has been installed on and around site, the following should be considered for mitigating light pollution:

- only use lighting as required (eg for safety reasons)
- use an appropriate powered light. The maximum considered to be suitable for exterior security lighting is 2000 lumens or 150w
- install movement sensors with timers, as this will reduce the amount of time a certain area is constantly lit
- position/direct* lighting away from sensitive receptors

* Note that less than 70 degrees from the vertical is a general rule of thumb.

The alternative to using traditional security lighting is to install infrared security systems. This method removes the need to illuminate areas as infrared light is not visible.

Respond to any complaints received and implement mitigation measures where possible. Complaints from local residents to the local authority can mean the identification of a statutory nuisance and an abatement notice being served.

Energy consumption/wastage

Controlling the amount of light pollution generated on site not only reduces and/or mitigates nuisance and disturbance, but it also reduces the energy used and wasted on site.

Good practice for reducing energy consumption and waste from lighting is included within the checklists (see **Section 4.4.2.4**).

4.4.2.4 Good practice checklists

Controlling light pollution	✓
Identify sensitive receptors and position/direct light away from them	
Use directional lighting	
Avoid excessive lighting	
Light areas only when required	
Install lighting accessories to reduce/mitigate light spillage, eg hoods, shields, reflectors	
Implement 'switch off' schemes	
Install motion sensors and timers	
Use appropriate power levels of illumination	
Install features to reduce lighting, eg 'last man out' switch, infrared security lighting	

Reduce lighting energy consumption	✓
Avoid excessive lighting	
Light areas only when required	
Implement 'switch off' schemes	
Install motion sensors and timers	
Use appropriate power levels of illumination	
Install energy efficient lighting, eg light-emitting diode (LED) and Halogen bulbs	

4.4.2.5 Legislation

Legislation is constantly changing, including amendments and new legislation, and this varies between England, Wales, Scotland and Northern Ireland. If site staff are unsure on any environmental issue, contact the regional environmental regulator for advice.

Legislation	Key requirements	Applicable Nation(s)
Clean Neighbourhoods and Environment Act (Northern Ireland) 2011	Sets out rules on statutory nuisance, which could lead to the issuing of an abatement notice by the local authority.	Northern Ireland
The Nature Conservation (Scotland) Act 2004	Sets out the system to define and control SSSI or the best examples of Scottish natural heritage of wildlife habitats, geological features and landforms. Also makes provisions for the protection of land from weeds such as Japanese knotweed. Lists species protected from disturbance, injury, intentional destruction or sale, eg nesting birds.	Scotland
Environmental Protection Act 1990	Under Section 80 local authorities can serve an abatement notice upon the cause of a statutory nuisance to stop work immediately.	England, Wales, Scotland
Wildlife and Countryside Act 1981 (as amended)	The major legal instrument for wildlife protection in Britain. It is divided into four parts covering protection of wildlife, designation of protected areas, public rights of way, and miscellaneous provisions. It sets out the system to define and control SSSIs and the best examples of natural heritage of wildlife habitats, geological features and landforms. It also makes provisions for the protection of land from weeds such as Japanese knotweed and lists species protected from disturbance, injury, intentional destruction or sale, eg nesting birds.	England, Wales
Control of Pollution Act (CoPA) 1974	Local authorities can serve a Section 60 notice if the conditions of the Section 61 consent are breached or if there is no Section 61 in place and excessive noise is being produced.	England, Wales, Scotland
The Wildlife (Northern Ireland) Order, 1985 (as amended)	Makes it an offence to intentionally kill, injure, or take any wild bird or their eggs or nests. The Order also prohibits certain methods of recklessly killing, injuring, or taking birds, restricts the sale and possession of captive bred birds, and sets standards for keeping birds in captivity. Similar rules apply to wild animals. It also protects badgers and invasive species controls.	Northern Ireland

4.4.3　Noise and vibration

4.4.3.1　Why is noise and vibration management important?

Excessive noise on site not only represents a major hazard to site staff, but can annoy neighbours and in some cases disturb nearby wildlife whether it occurs on a single or numerous occasions – with the latter leading to cumulative impact occurring. Excessive noise and vibration can cause the following:

- poor quality of life for affected residents (ie disturbance, stress and health impacts)
- complaints
- structural damage to buildings and utilities
- wildlife disturbance.

And lead to:

- statutory enforcement of controls by the local authority or court that could lead to prosecution resulting in revisions to working methods, working hours and even stopping of the works

- programme delays and associated costs
- damage to third party and community relations
- damage to corporate/project reputation
- damage to wildlife habitats.

Effective planning, on-site management of noise and traffic management (see **Section 4.6**), will significantly reduce the likelihood of any of these actions being taken, and so reduce the risk of construction noise affecting the overall performance of a project. Understanding, adopting, communicating and integrating the legal requirement to employ BPM to minimise noise and vibration at all times and all locations, is the best way to indicate to the local authorities, local residents and construction workers that noise and vibration is being managed satisfactorily on site.

4.4.3.2 What is noise?

Noise is commonly referred to as unwanted sound. Sound is a wave transmitted as small changes in air pressure (known as sound pressure) between a source and receiver (ie a construction site and a nearby resident). It should be noted that vibration is very similar to noise except that the vibration wave is transmitted through the ground or solid object. The legal definition of noise includes vibration. Excessive noise is the single most common source of complaint against the construction industry, and can result in work being stopped on site.

Noise units

The measure of sound pressure level is the decibel (dB) and it is based on a logarithmic scale. A sound level meter is used to measure noise and can measure different parameters and weighting. The A-weighting scale is often used as it corresponds most closely to the frequency response of the human ear. Typically, in respect of construction noise the indices most frequently measured are the period noise level (L_{Aeq}) and the maximum noise level (L_{Amax}).

Propagation

The level of noise observed from a construction activity at a nearby building depends on several factors, some of which can be controlled on site while others rely on local conditions. To manage noise on site, consideration should be given to those factors that can be controlled, namely:

- the noise level of the activity (determined by construction method and plant selection)
- the likely frequency of the noise to minimise the cumulative impact occurring
- level of screening between the noise source and the receiver point
- location of the activity within the construction site (if possible).

Environmental alert: noise nuisance

4.3

Background

A serious environmental incident occurred on a project in London where the local environmental health department issued a letter of caution following a series of noise related offences affecting local neighbours.

The offences constituted a breach of the Section 60 notice (Control of Pollution Act 1974) that was previously served on the site, which is an abatement notice stating that no noisy operations should be taking place outside of normal working hours.

Conclusion

Due to the conditions of the Section 60 being breached, the council is considering legal action against the project, which may lead to fines and prosecution.

Actions for all projects where there is a risk of affecting neighbours due to noise and/or vibration

1   Always ensure work is carried out within agreed hours and noise limited unless otherwise approved.

2   Contact appropriate colleagues and local environmental health officer to discuss the programme of works and potential impacts.

3   Consider applying for Section 61 consent (UK only). This is a formal and legal agreement between the project and the local authority to agree noise levels and hours of work to mitigate the effect on the local community. Section 61 protects communities from local authority action under Section 60, as long as the Section 61 conditions are not breached.

4   Arrange for noise/vibration monitoring at sensitive locations.

Actions for all projects/locations:

1   Contact appropriate colleagues to discuss noise/vibrations related risks.

2   Engage the local environmental health officer to discuss the programme of works, if appropriate consider applying for a Section 61 consent or other local agreement with regulatory authorities.

3   If a Section 60 or other official notice relating to noise or other nuisance is received, ensure the legal department and sustainability teams are notified and record on YellowJacket.

Local conditions that cannot normally be controlled on site are:

●   distance from the noise source to the building

●   reflections from nearby buildings

●   ground absorption

●   atmospheric conditions (ie wind direction, humidity and temperature).

Effective planning

Careful planning of the construction works to take all reasonable and practicable steps to minimise noise and vibration, can significantly reduce the amount of disturbance and reduce the risk of noise abatement action. This includes liaison with the local authority and environmental health officer. This approach is encouraged as it provides a great deal of certainty to delivering construction projects with agreed methodologies and noise levels.

Best practicable means (BPM)

BPM, defined within legislation, is a balancing of noise and vibration factors and it means that mitigation or working constraints can be prioritised to those locations and activities, which are most required. For example:

- **proximity of works to residents** – the further away from residents that works occur the less mitigation is required to demonstrate BPM (eg 500 m away opposed to only 50 m)
- **duration** – if an activity is required to be undertaken only for a few days, then it may require significantly less mitigation than if it was to be undertaken for several weeks
- **time of day** – works undertaken at night require more mitigation and justification than works during the day
- **engineering practicability and safety** – if there is no alternative but to undertake the works at night with noisy equipment (because there is no quieter equipment that exists to do the work) then this would constitute BPM, as long as detailed justification was given and local residents were informed in advance of the works.

Other factors include cost, current state of technical knowledge/techniques and number of residents affected.

The following generic measures should be considered in the pursuance of BPM, in order of priority:

- control of noise at source
- selection of low noise methods, eg vibro-piling or super silenced generators
- control of working hours
- selection of quiet or low noise equipment
- location of equipment on site
- correct orientation of plant and equipment, ie ensure piling rig is facing away from sensitive receptors during impact piling operations
- provision of acoustic enclosures
- screening
- local screening of plant
- site perimeter hoarding
- create a one-way system to prevent unnecessary traffic movements.

If noisy activities have to be undertaken near residents over long periods then consideration can be given under BPM to provide protection. For example sound insulation to windows and ventilation at properties or temporary relocation of residents as a last resort. These approaches may be considered as BPM only if it can be demonstrated that all other forms of BPM (eg noise control at source) have been exhausted.

4.4.3.3 Pre-construction noise monitoring

Before the works start the ambient and background noise levels at locations around the site should be monitored as part of a noise survey. The results should be used to plan the location of noisy operations that could cause nuisance to sensitive receptors, and can be used to oppose any unsubstantiated complaints.

On-site management

On-site management should continue beyond the planning stage taking the good practices and BPM measures identified to minimise noise and vibration, and ensuring that they are adopted on site.

Note that the legislation relates to the actual construction methods. Noise on site should be managed through:

- inspections ensuring that BPM has been adopted (ie correct working hours)
- monitoring to confirm noise level of site activities
- identifying and reporting non-BPM practices, so they can be rectified
- revising working practices to ensure that BPM is adopted at all times
- repeating inspections at regular intervals during the project, but more frequently during particularly noisy activities.

Community liaison should be undertaken in advance of any noisy works (eg letter drops, information on a project website or at local community facilities). This will provide information on what activities will be carried out on site, the reasons why these works are needed and the duration of noisy activities. Contact information should be provided to the local authority and nearby sensitive receptors in order to ensure that any disturbance that might occur can be managed appropriately. The value of good community liaison cannot be overstated. Giving prior warning of particularly disruptive works can lead to more tolerant neighbour relations and even agreement to higher noise levels or specific times of operation, where the overall benefits are perceived by residents as being positive.

Information should be sought from the community concerning sensitive periods (eg school exams), so works can be planned outside these times. If working times have been agreed, it is important to ensure that these are adhered to. Through developing and maintaining good relations, the potential for complaints or civil claims in the long-term should be reduced.

It is important to remind site-based staff of their obligation to minimise noise and vibration on site. It is especially important to avoid unexpected early morning starts. This can be achieved in the site inductions, toolbox talks and through signage on-site.

4.4.3.4 Control of noise at source

Selection of low noise methods

The best way to minimise the possible disturbance to residents is to minimise the amount of noise generated in the first place, ideally by selection of low noise generating methods. Some of the construction activities that cause the greatest problems are:

- piling (particularly by diesel hammer)
- breaking out with pneumatic tools
- scabbling of concrete
- falling ball demolition
- grit-blasting
- hydro-demolition
- high pitched reversing alarms.

These methods should be used only when all other practicable methods have been investigated and discounted or when their use minimises other environmental impacts. For example, hydro-demolition is noisy but the level of dust produced in comparison to conventional demolition methods is significantly less. So in certain situations it may be preferable to prioritise the control of dust rather than noise.

Working hours

The level of disturbance resulting from noise associated with a construction site activity is dependent on when and where the noise occurs. In residential areas people are more sensitive to noise in the evening, at night, at the weekend or on a bank holiday, compared to the normal working week. So, where possible works should be limited to weekday daytime only.

In certain industrial/office areas, where the nearby properties are unoccupied during the evening and at the weekend, it may be better to programme noisy activities for during these periods.

For mixed residential and office buildings consider 'quiet periods' during the daytime when certain noisy activities (eg piling) are not undertaken to minimise the effect on the office buildings. To balance the loss of daytime hours, work into the early evening or begin works earlier.

To limit the impact of a project on the local community, the local authority may stipulate the hours that noisy works are permitted, or it may restrict working hours by placing a limit on the average noise allowed over a given period. In these cases, if the noise exceeds the limit set, the working period should be reduced or an alternative and quieter work method adopted.

Selection of quiet or low noise equipment

For many construction activities there are several items of plant that could be used to undertake a particular task, eg use of hydraulic jack method over impact drop hammer. In some circumstances the use of a single larger item of equipment rather than several small items of equipment can reduce noise levels on site, eg use of a single generator opposed to several smaller generators. Ensure all plant and equipment is well maintained and is turned off when not in use. Where activities occur in close proximity to sensitive receptors and especially residential properties at night, consideration should be given to 'super silent' generators, the use of mains electricity where possible and the use of innovative technologies (eg hydrogen fuel cells).

Provision of acoustic enclosures

Some equipment can be supplied with acoustic enclosures, such as hoods and doors on compressors and generators, or other noise control devices such as jackets on pneumatic drills and shrouds on piling rigs and cranes. These devices should not only be closed, but also be tight fitting and well-sealed. A partly closed door is of little use.

Screening

If designed and used correctly, screening (**Figure 4.32**) can considerably reduce noise levels from a site and at relatively low cost. Screening can be provided by existing buildings, earth bunds, site material storage, site security hoarding, or purpose built noise screens.

As a general rule any screening should be placed as close as possible to either the source or receiver in order that there is no 'line of sight' (**Figure 4.33**).

Figure 4.32   *Acoustic screening (courtesy BAM Nuttall)*

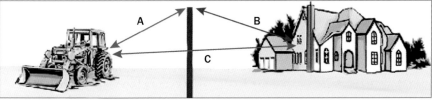

Figure 4.33   *Noise screen configuration (midway between source and receiver)*

The increase in distance between a noise source and receiver over (or around) a screen compared to the direct distance path (path difference) can be expressed as:

Path difference = (distance A + distance B) – distance C

The amount of sound passing through the noise screen is controlled by:

1   Density of the screen material (generally the higher the density the lower the level of sound passing through the barrier).

2   Any holes/openings within the noise screen.

The configuration of the screen can be changed to suit individual site requirements, while still achieving maximum noise reduction:

● screen is midway between the source and receiver, but with an increased screen height

● screen is moved closer to the source

● screen is moved closer to the receiver.

There are a number of proprietary absorbent noise screens that can be hung from standard Heras site fencing. These have gained in popularity due to the ease of use and ability to be used in a variety of formations as site specific noise sources change by type or location. Generally the maximum reduction can be achieved by using purpose-built screen or site security hoarding.

> Be sure that the noise screen solution adopted for a site is inspected to ensure no gaps are present. If the source of the noise (ie the site) is close to a sensitive receiver liaise with a specialist for advice on the sort of screen required.

4.4.3.5   Specific BPM measures to minimise noise and vibration

Specific mitigation measures, which should be adopted where appropriate to demonstrate BPM, involve:

● careful selection of equipment, construction methods and programming with the objective of reducing noise and vibration where possible. Only equipment, including road vehicles, conforming to relevant national or international standards, directives and recommendations on noise and vibration emissions, should be used

● using noise-control equipment such as jackets, shrouds, hoods, and doors, and ensuring they are closed (see the previous section on *Provision of acoustic enclosures*)

● erecting hoardings or screens as noise barriers before any construction activities are undertaken

● locating plant, as far as is reasonably practicable, away from receptors or as close as possible to noise barriers or hoardings where these are located between the source and receptor (see *Provision of acoustic enclosures*)

- using solid doors and gates that should not be located opposite sensitive receptors. The operation of gates should be controlled to minimise the time they are open for the passage of vehicles, reducing stray noise emissions

- ensuring that all plant is maintained regularly to comply with relevant national or international standards

- ensuring that air lines are maintained and checked regularly to prevent leaks

- operating plant in the mode of operation that minimises noise emissions

- ensuring that plant is shut down when not in use

- prohibiting works vehicles waiting or queuing on the public highway

- constructing temporary infrastructure (eg haul roads) of materials that minimise noise and vibration (eg laying a tarmac surface)

- avoiding percussive piling, except where there is an overriding justification

- using bending as opposed to percussion methods to break out concrete. Rotary drills and bursters actuated by hydraulic or electrical power should be used for excavating hard material. In some instances chemical bursting can be used where nearby sensitive structures are particularly vulnerable to vibration from pneumatic breakers etc

- handling all materials, particularly steelwork, in a manner that minimises noise. For example storing materials as far as possible away from sensitive receptors and using resilient mats around steel handling areas

- designing all audible warning systems and alarms to minimise noise. Non-audible warning systems can be used in preference, ie cab-mounted CCTV or the use of banksmen. If required, ensure that audible warning systems are switched to the minimum setting required by the Health and Safety Executive (HSE), and where practicable use 'white noise' reversing alarms in place of the usual 'siren' style reversing alert

- designing haul routes to minimise the amount of reversing required

- selecting electrically powered plant that is quieter than diesel or petrol-driven plant, if interchangeable

- fitting suitable anti-vibration mountings where practicable, to rotating and/or impacting equipment.

Consent

For some construction projects especially projects in residential/built up areas, it is advisable to make an application for consent, otherwise known as a Section 61 consent, to the relevant local authority before works begin (not applicable in Northern Ireland). The advantages of applying for consent are that:

● the project can programme works as far as possible in advance to minimise the risk of local authority intervention (subject to compliance with the conditions within the consent from the local authority)

● the risk of delay costs due to abatement action can be reduced

● the formal acceptance by the local authority that BPM has been adopted.

4.4.3.6 Construction noise monitoring

During construction, regular inspections should be undertaken to ensure that the noise and vibration minimising methods, plant and mitigation identified in the planning stage are adopted on site and are working effectively.

Formal inspections should be undertaken by operatives at all times. It may occur at the same frequency and in conjunction with any health and safety review (probably once a week). If applicable, it is recommended that construction method inspections should be integrated into any health and safety or quality surveillance regime.

Environmental noise monitoring

The need to undertake noise monitoring may be a requirement of the contract or it may arise out of a consent agreement with the local authority.

It is recommended that noise monitoring be undertaken at the start of each new activity. This may mean that monitoring is required on a daily basis during the first weeks of a construction project, but subject to satisfactory results, this could be relaxed to once a week/twice-weekly depending upon the site activities. The frequency should be increased again if particularly noisy activities (such as driven piling) are undertaken.

The monitoring data can be used to assess compliance with any noise limits specified, noise level predictions within a Section 61 consent application, or change in noise levels compared with any pre-construction noise monitoring.

The duration of the monitoring on any one day is important. BS 5228-1:2009+A1:2014 suggests that the average noise level over a day can be approximated within certain tolerances by taking short-term measurements throughout the day, eg five minutes in every hour. However, the nature of the individual noise sources and the length of time noise from any one plant item or operation is sustained will determine the extent to which short-term measurements can accurately reflect the noise climate in any one hour or extended period.

Environmental noise monitoring should be undertaken only by suitably-trained and experienced staff. Where the requirements for noise monitoring occur as a result of a Section 61 consent, then advice from the local authority environmental health officer (EHO) should be sought as to the requirements for noise monitoring, ie where to measure and for how long. The following information is given to help site-based staff ensure monitoring is being properly carried out.

How and where to measure

A suitably qualified acoustic consultant or company employee, should be employed to provide technical advice and define where and when to measure. Advice should be sought from a qualified acoustician with regard to the relevant parameters to measure and the type of assessment required. The choice of appropriate measurement equipment is essential in order to ensure that the correct acoustic parameters are measured and that any such measurements are robust and stand up to scrutiny from other parties. In this respect all equipment should be calibrated in-line with the requirements of any relevant British Standards (eg BS 5228-1:2009+A1:2014) or other guidance documents.

Figure 4.34   Façade noise monitoring equipment (courtesy Arup)

In sensitive areas noise measurement (**Figure 4.34**) may be specified as a contract requirement. It is good practice to employ an acoustician for this activity if there is a likelihood of the site works creating noise disturbance, or nuisance. Where noise monitoring is required it should be carried out in-line with any relevant British Standards (eg BS 5228-1:2009+A1:2014) or other guidance document, the requirements of any site noise and vibration management plan or EMP and ANC (2013).

For long-term and possibly unmanned noise and vibration monitoring, extra care should be taken in locating the measurement equipment to minimise both the risk of damage or theft and the influence of other external noise sources, eg fixed building services plant.

Site management need to remain in contact with the person responsible for taking measurements to ensure that the measuring equipment (**Figure 4.35**) will not be affected, or changes will be managed to maintain valid measurements, by changes to the site as the project progresses.

4.4.3.7 Why is vibration management important?

High vibration levels over a sustained period can cause damage to buildings, while lower vibration levels can cause disturbance, annoyance and stress to residents. By properly informing local residents of the likelihood that vibration will occur, the less likely they are to complain or experience stress.

How to avoid vibration problems

The primary aims in the management of vibration on site are to avoid:

- causing annoyance and concerns
- being (falsely) accused of causing damage
- causing damage to nearby structures.

The following six steps will help in addressing each of these aims:

1 **Evaluate the potential for vibration and damage**

Figure 4.35 *Free-field noise monitoring equipment (courtesy Parsons Brinckerhoff)*

Transmission of vibration is highly dependent on ground conditions and on features in the ground, such as pipe runs. Prediction methods do exist, but they require specialist expertise to implement and rely on detailed information being available on the site, the ground conditions and the plant.

If it appears that a piling or ground engineering project will generate vibration putting nearby structures at risk, then a detailed study should be undertaken by specialists. In most other situations it should be sufficient for staff to review the operations to take place on site and establish the sensitive areas around the site that may need to be monitored.

2 **Monitor conditions before works start**

Before starting the construction operations, it is important to survey the condition of identified sensitive locations and structures. The survey should include a detailed record of:

a   Existing cracks and their widths.

b   Level and plumb survey, including damp-proof course measurements of tilting walls or bulges.

c   Other existing damage including loose or broken tiles, pipes, gullies or plaster.

Photographic records and installation of measuring devices are helpful to establish alleged or actual damage. In some situations it will be necessary to strengthen vulnerable off-site structures before vibrations start.

Sensitive locations to survey and monitor before and during construction would include:

a   Aquatic habitats nearby.

b   Brittle/ancient underground services including tunnels.

c   Buildings in poor condition.

d   Historic buildings.

e   Hospitals and nursing homes.

f   Housing.

g   Laboratories.

h   Museums.

i   Precision machine workshops.

j   Schools.

k   Sensitive plant or equipment used by local companies.

3   Inform neighbours

Vibration causes anxiety and annoyance to residents mostly because they fear that it will cause damage. It is useful to explain to people that damage only occurs at vibration levels many times greater than those that can normally be felt from construction plant.

Informing neighbours of the potential for vibration allows site-based staff to learn of any particularly sensitive issues that may be time-dependent and that may be resolved by limiting hours of work.

4   Minimise effects during works

The adoption of BPM to minimise noise and vibration should have identified the best low vibration method for the completion of a construction task. If there are further concerns about the vibration impact of a construction method then they should be revisited at this stage.

The following specific BPM measures should be considered:

a   Can the activity be undertaken using a different methodology that results in lower levels of vibration at the nearby sensitive receptor?

b   As high frequency vibration causes less damage than low frequency vibration, can the plant be operated in a mode that generates less low frequency vibration (eg vibratory roller, wacker-plates)?

c   Can the plant be isolated from the transfer medium (ie what it's sitting on)? Can plant be placed on a heavy base, which causes less vibration than plant on a lighter base (eg mount plant on the ground rather than on suspended structures)?

5   Monitor vibration levels during the works

To be effective, monitoring of vibration levels should be carried out by trained staff or by external specialists. However, it may be necessary for site-based staff to discuss with building occupants where vibration monitoring can be conducted.

When monitoring at properties during operations, the two main rules are:

a   Measure inside rooms when assessing for nuisance, noting that the choice of measurement position and extraneous vibration events such as footfall and the slamming of doors may affect the measurement results.

b   Measure on the structure outside when assessing for damage (doorsteps are a good location).

It should be noted that vibration measurement at premises is often impracticable and it is only possible to measure externally at the site or sensitive premises boundary. In which case a transfer function will have to be derived for the local ground conditions, an allowance made for attenuation between ground and foundation and possible amplification at the higher storeys of sensitive premises.

Do not forget that in sensitive structures continued visual monitoring and measurement of crack widths is the best way to determine whether actual damage is being caused.

6   Monitor conditions after works are completed.

The same evaluation as undertaken for Step 2 should be carried out and results compared to the precondition surveys.

4.4.3.8   Good practice checklists

Noise	
Change the working method to use equipment or modes of operation that produce less noise. For example: • in demolition works use hydraulic shears in place of hydraulic impact breakers • in driving steel sheet piles consider the jacking method (subject to soil conditions, eg cohesive soils), which produce only a fraction of the noise of conventional hammer-driven piling • when breaking out pavements consider other methods than pneumatic breakers and drills, including chemical splitters or falling weight breakers	
Reduce the need for noisy assembly practices, eg fabricate off site	
Keep noisy plant as far away as possible from sensitive receptors	
Adopt working hours to restrict noisy activities to certain less sensitive periods of the day	
Arrange delivery times to suit the area – daytime for residential areas, perhaps night time for commercial inner city areas	
Route construction vehicles to take account of the need to reduce noise and vibration	
Keep haul roads well maintained	
Use mufflers or silencers to reduce noise transmitted along pipes and ducts	

Minimise the drop height into hoppers, lorries or other plant (reducing the drop height by a factor of 10, which reduces noise by about 10 dB)	
Consider using rubber linings on tippers at very sensitive sites	
Liaise with SNCOs to minimise noise disturbance (disruption) to any sensitive wildlife	

Screens	✓
Where possible, place sources of noise away from sensitive receptors	
Avoid locations where multiple reflections of noise might result in increased receptor noise levels	
Erect the screen close to the source(s) of noise or the receptor	
Build the screen from materials with density of 7 kg/m^2 or higher, with panels stiffened to prevent drumming	
For the most effective results build the screen about one metre above the highest sight line	
Seal all gaps and openings, including gaps at the bottom of the screen	
Glaze any public observation openings in perimeter hoardings with Perspex (protected with wire mesh or similar) if sensitive receptors are lower than the height of the hoarding	
Consider placing more screens close to sensitive receptors but not parallel to nearby walls, unless the screens are of the absorbent variety	

Vibration	✓
Change the working method to use equipment or modes of operation that produce less vibration, for example: • breaking out concrete, where practicable, should be undertaken using equipment that breaks by bending rather than by percussion • where practicable, rotary drills and bursters actuated by hydraulic or electrical power should be used for excavating hard material	
Undertake vibration activities as far away as possible from sensitive receptors	
Adopt working hours to restrict high vibration generating activities to certain periods of the day	
Suitable anti-vibration mountings should be fitted where practicable to rotating and/or impacting equipment	
Keep haul roads well maintained	
Consider using rubber linings on tippers in sensitive sites	

4.4.3.9 Further reading

ANC (2012) *Red Book: Measurement and assessment of groundborne noise and vibration (second edition)*, Association of Noise Consultants, St Albans, UK.
Go to: **www.association-of-noise-consultants.co.uk/Publications_Guidelines**

BS 7385-2:1993 *Evaluation and measurement for vibration in buildings. Guide to damage levels from groundborne vibration*

BS 5228-2: 2009+A1:2014 *Code of practice for noise and vibration control on construction and open sites. Vibration*

BS ISO 4866:2010 *Mechanical vibration and shock. Vibration of fixed structures. Guidelines for the measurement of vibrations and evaluation of their effects on structures*

4.4.3.10 Legislation

Legislation is constantly changing, including amendments and new legislation, and this varies between England, Wales, Scotland and Northern Ireland. If site staff are unsure on any environmental issue, contact the regional environmental regulator for advice.

Legislation	Key requirements	Applicable Nation(s)
Clean Neighbourhoods and Environment Act (Northern Ireland) 2011	Sets out rules on statutory nuisance, including noise, which could lead to the issuing of an abatement notice by the local authority.	Northern Ireland
Environmental Protection Act 1990 (as amended)	Under Section 80 local authorities can serve an abatement notice upon the cause of a statutory nuisance to stop work immediately.	England, Wales, Scotland, Northern Ireland
Control of Pollution Act (CoPA) 1974	A local authority can serve a Section 60 notice if the conditions of the Section 61 consent are breached or if there is no Section 61 in place and excessive noise is being produced.	England, Wales, Scotland
The Noise Emissions in the Environment by Equipment for use Outdoors Regulations 2001 (as amended)	The intention of the legislation is to control and monitor noise of equipment for use outdoors. Construction plant and equipment must carry an appropriate label to indicate that it conforms to the levels given in the Regulations for that type of machinery.	England
Construction Plant and Equipment (Harmonisation of Noise Emission Standards) Regulations 1985 and 1988 (as amended) The Construction Plant and Equipment (Harmonisation of Noise Emission Standards) (Extension to Northern Ireland) Regulations 1992 (as amended)	An EC examination certificate is required before any item of construction plant and equipment may be marketed. Construction plant and equipment must carry an EC mark to indicate that it conforms to the levels given in the Regulations for that type of machinery. Failure to comply with, or contravention of, the Regulations may result in a fine of up to £2000.	England, Wales, Scotland, Northern Ireland
The Pollution Control and Local Government (NI) Order 1978	Complaints can be made against a noise or vibration source under Article 39. Magistrates can then serve an abatement notice upon the cause of a statutory nuisance to stop work immediately.	Northern Ireland

4.5 RESOURCE MANAGEMENT

4.5.1 Energy consumption

4.5.1.1 Introduction

The reduction of energy is closely linked to GHG emissions and climate change. The primary focus has been placed on carbon emissions. Carbon is the most prevalent of all the GHG emissions and it is used as an indicator in the Climate Change Act 2008. The Act has set legally binding targets, from the 1990 baseline, of a 34 per cent reduction in carbon emissions by 2020 and an 80 per cent reduction by 2050. This also includes the establishment of other requirements and commitments. Carbon also features, for example, in the scoring opportunities for BREEAM and CEEQUAL (see Section 1.4).

These requirements place a responsibility on all industries and individuals to reduce their energy consumption, especially energy generated through the burning of fossil fuels. There are opportunities to reduce energy consumption through design, advance programming, embodied energy and energy management at corporate offices among others.

Optimising material needs to reduce embodied carbon (courtesy Galliford Try plc and Black & Veatch)

Background

The recondition of the River Irwell flood defence scheme in Salford required the installation of rock armour to support the toe of the embankment. An initial design was submitted and accepted for the use of 62 500 tonnes of rock armour. The project was put out to competitive tender and won by Galliford Try plc and Black & Veatch. These two companies reviewed the project and realised that some segments of the scheme could be reduced or omitted. So they submitted new designs that required only 15 600 tonnes of rock armour and reduced the project embodied carbon by 385 tonnes. The new design was accepted by the Environment Agency and the works proceeded to construction.

Lessons learnt

Implementing the change at the design stage allows significant costs and carbon reduction.

HM Government (2013) outlines a number of key targets for the construction industry to be achieved by 2025. In summary these are:

- 33 per cent reduction in the initial cost of construction and the whole-life cost of built assets

- 50 per cent reduction in the trade gap between total exports and total imports for construction products and materials

- 50 per cent reduction in the overall time, from inception to completion, for new build and refurbished assets

- 50 per cent reduction in GHG emissions in the built environment.

Activities on site can help to reduce the emission of GHGs from the built environment in a number of ways, for example by greater attention to the quality of joints to avoid air leakage reducing the amount of energy needed to heat a dwelling.

The choice of construction products can often be influenced during the construction phase. Comparing similar products in terms of embodied carbon can help to make a more informed choice regarding which substitutions are more significant in terms of the construction project. It is also possible that products with higher embodied impacts can have greater operation benefits. Materials may also be supplied from the local area of the project thereby reducing transport impacts, road congestion and associated safety concerns. Larger projects are more likely to have requirements promoting the use of a local supply chain.

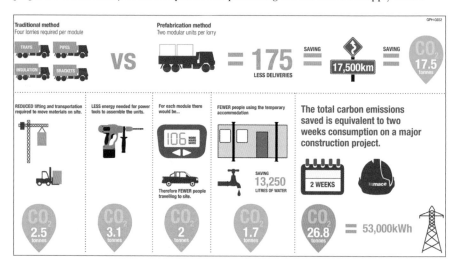

Figure 4.36   Reduction of carbon footprint through pre-fabrication (courtesy Mace)

4.5.1.2   Energy consumption during construction phases

Some construction projects will consume more energy than others during the use phase or operation. However, it is still important to control and minimise energy consumption during the construction phase. Indeed some projects will not use energy in operation making the construction impacts more significant in the life cycle of the project.

Energy consumption during the construction phases can be attributed to a variety of operations. These operations are identified as follows along with the measures that can be taken to reduce the energy consumption.

Construction plant and site vehicles

Construction plant is one of the biggest users of energy on construction sites. Efficient use of this machinery and fuel efficiency are the key for reducing their energy consumption.

Fuel efficiency can be achieved through selecting the right plant for the jobs, for example, avoid using oversized or undersized machines which would be inefficient. Also select plant based on their fuel efficiency credentials. Details of the fuel consumption are available from construction plant suppliers. Ensure that the construction plant owned by the organisation is regularly serviced. This will not only help fuel efficiency, but also the plants lifespan. Construction plant should avoid being left to run 'idle'.

Efficient use can be achieved through advanced operator training in driving plant efficiently and also a good works programme and plant positioning, so as to avoid unnecessary movements.

In terms of site vehicles consideration should be given to using hybrid and/or fully-electric vehicles to minimise emissions and reduce fuel consumption (**Figure 4.37**).

Figure 4.37   Electric site vehicle (courtesy BAM Nuttall)

Site topography

The optimisation of cut and fill for a construction site should be undertaken during design stage, but this can be improved upon during construction. Reducing the movement of vehicles and plant to take material off site could be minimised by reusing material on site or working with another project in the area (if feasible). This activity can reduce energy consumption, but also save on landfill costs and improve the resource efficiency. It would also be recommended to keep records of volumes of excavated materials that have been reused efficiently on site.

Deliveries and logistics

In some cases it is possible to access a site by a number of different roads. There may be restrictions on some due to schools etc but the most efficient route could be promoted by the placement of signage to direct deliveries to site. Transport impacts can also be reduced by car sharing and works mini-buses. National logistics companies can provide telemetry services that help to plan deliveries more effectively and give real time data that can also be helpful in arranging back haul routes for surplus materials and waste removal. The on-site management of delivery vehicles can also lead to reduced energy consumption, ie less time idling waiting for a space to be cleared for the products to be off loaded.

Site accommodation

Temporary offices and associated cabins, for example, canteens and changing rooms, are often poorly insulated, glazed, heated and lit. The use of modern temporary offices and

Figure 4.38   Energy signage (courtesy Laing   Figure 4.39   Switch-off notice (courtesy BAM
              O'Rourke)   Nuttall)

cabins reduce energy consumption through better insulation, glazing, lighting (eg motion sensors), heating and electricity (eg meters and master switch off).

A focus on the occupants of these offices and cabins can also lead to a reduction in consumption from raising awareness (**Figures 4.38** and **4.39**) and encouraging behaviour change through training and 'switch off' schemes.

Utilities

Often site utilities can consume energy. When gaining access to utilities such as water and electricity it is worthwhile checking that the associated mechanical and electrical equipment (pumps etc) are not unnecessarily oversized and therefore consume more energy during construction than is really needed.

Grid connection

It is considered that connection of a site to the national grid is more energy efficient than relying on power from diesel generators. So, where possible the connection should be established as early as practicable.

It may also be possible (depending on the scale of the project) to incorporate low or zero carbon energy for the construction phase. This could be in the form of solar photovoltaic panels and wind turbines, but also alternative lower carbon fuels for mobile plant and delivery vehicles could be considered.

Metrics and reporting

The performance of construction projects is often assessed through schemes such as BREEAM and CEEQUAL (see **Section 1.4**). There is a requirement to demonstrate sustainability performance, which is derived from data recorded at the site level. It is good practice to record energy consumption data for the most significant aspects of the construction as these will not only assist in identifying areas for improvement, but serve as evidence in the latter sustainability assessment of the project.

Most large construction companies report to stakeholders on their sustainability performance through an annual report. Data is often gathered from each project and office to be aggregated up to the corporate level. Site level data is the most valuable as it varies by construction project and one of the greatest areas for improvement for many businesses.

General energy management

The following points should also be considered when on site to reduce energy consumption.

- switch off electrical equipment and lighting when not required
- ensure windows and doors are closed in cold weather and seals are in good condition
- report defective seals, electrical equipment, lighting, heating/cooling
- turn off/turn down heating in unoccupied offices or cabins
- install energy efficient lighting
- avoid unnecessary night time site and accommodation lighting.

Reducing energy consumption will not only reduce the environmental impact of the construction site but also the release of GHGs, reduce waste, improve resource efficiency and help to lower costs.

4.5.1.3 Further reading

KO, J (2010) *Carbon: Reducing the footprint of the construction industry. An action plan to reduce carbon emissions*, Report 006, Strategic Forum for Construction and the Carbon Trust, UK. Go to: **www.strategicforum.org.uk/pdf/06carbonreducingfootprint.pdf**

4.5.1.4 Legislation

Legislation is constantly changing, including amendments and new legislation, and this varies between England, Wales, Scotland and Northern Ireland. If site staff are unsure on any environmental issue, contact the regional environmental regulator for advice.

Legislation	Key requirements	Applicable Nation(s)
Climate Change Act 2008	Sets out a framework for moving the UK to a low-carbon economy, as progress continues towards establishing a post-2012 global emissions agreement. There are no specific legislative requirements on businesses specifically to reduce their carbon footprints, the UK Government has signed up a range of targets to reduce carbon emissions (eg Kyoto Protocol and Climate Change Levy [CCL]).	England, Wales, Scotland, Northern Ireland
The Climate Change Levy (General) Regulations 2001 (as amended) Finance Act 2013	The CCL is an energy tax rather than a carbon tax. It is aimed at industry, including agriculture and the public sector, and applies to all non-household use of coal, gas, electricity and non-transport liquefied petroleum gas (LPG). Climate change agreements can be set for energy-intensive industries to set targets for agreed emission reductions in return for CCL discount.	England, Wales, Scotland, Northern Ireland

4.5.2 Materials

4.5.2.1 Efficient use of materials

Using resources efficiently is important for reducing environmental impact, reducing waste and minimising costs. Increasingly, clients and contractors require monitoring and reporting on resource efficiency. This feeds into corporate reporting on carbon, water, waste and cost. It also helps to ensure materials are being ordered, used, managed and disposed of effectively.

A useful tool for this is a RMP, which is invaluable in identifying where opportunities to maximise efficient use of resources can be identified before works start, and throughout the construction process (**Figure 4.40**).

There are two aspects to environmental good practice in relation to materials:

1   Using materials more efficiently.

2   Using more sustainable materials.

Efficient use of materials saves cost and waste. It was once common practice that an extra five to 10 per cent of materials was 'over-ordered' to allow for site waste through damage, spills, under-supply and vandalism. These figures can be reduced. The materials resource efficiency checklist (see **Section 4.5.2.7**) can be used to focus on how materials are ordered, delivered, stored and handled on site and to help investigate how to reduce waste.

Choosing more sustainable materials reduces environmental impacts, and can also have social and economic benefits. Clients and designers are now more frequently looking to choose more sustainable materials, particularly in categories that have significant environmental or social impacts. In some product categories, such as timber, product suppliers have developed more sustainable products that have detailed Chain of Custody (CoC) or EU Ecolabel requirements to demonstrate they provide a more sustainable solution. There are many UK-based, local providers of sustainable building materials.

Figure 4.40   Shredded vegetation retained on site as footpath chippings (courtesy BAM Nuttall)

4.5.2.2 Environmental impact

Materials selection and use on site can have several direct and indirect environmental impacts (see **Table 4.3**):

Table 4.3   *Example of environmental impacts*

Material	Direct impacts	Indirect impacts
Timber	<ul><li>depletion of resources</li><li>destruction of habitat</li><li>killing of flora and fauna</li><li>release of CO_2 from logging.</li></ul>	<ul><li>use of fossil fuels to cut trees and transport timber</li><li>waste produced in further treatment and use on site</li><li>emissions (CO_2, NO_x, SO_x etc) in transport</li><li>reduction in biodiversity.</li></ul>
Aggregates	<ul><li>depletion of finite resource</li><li>pollution during extraction and processing</li><li>visual impact and loss of land.</li></ul>	<ul><li>emissions (CO_2, NO_x, SO_x etc) in transport</li><li>waste generated through use.</li></ul>

These are two simplified examples of how commonly used construction materials can affect the environment. Most materials that are used in construction can have a negative effect on the environment and as a consequence a sustainable approach to the procurement and use of materials on site to reduce them is essential.

Construction assessment schemes such as BREEAM, CEEQUAL, DREAM and LEED consider materials selection to have a significant environmental impact on projects. Inappropriate materials selection during the construction phase is likely to affect the overall scheme award (see **Section 1.4**).

It is good practice to consider the link between material selection, use on site, waste management, carbon and water. This is referred to as resource efficiency and is the first step towards effective waste management and ultimately generating minimal waste.

Use of precast concrete to reduce embodied energy (courtesy Barhale Trant Utilities and Carlow Precast)

Background

Barhale Trant Utilities (BTU) were installing two humus tanks and a deep bed sand filter as part of the upgrade of the wastewater treatment works at Ashford. To reduce potable water consumption and the embodied carbon (29 per cent of onsite pouring emission) of the project, the tanks were to be precast units produced with rainwater.

Lessons learnt

Precast concrete solutions and rainwater use for construction products limit carbon footprint.

4.5.2.3 Material procurement

Important considerations when sourcing materials

Responsible sourcing and management of materials should ensure that the environmental, social and economic impacts associated with those materials are minimised.

All materials contain natural resources, whether this is direct (ie timber) or indirect (ie oil in plastics). Material manufacture may consume large amounts of natural resources such as the fuel used to maintain high temperatures in the manufacture of cement. Some materials contain hazardous chemicals or consume or release hazardous chemicals during their manufacture, application or disposal.

> The Alliance for Sustainable Building Products (ASBP) is a cross sector, not for profit organisation, comprising, building product manufacturers and distributors, specifiers, designers, contractors, public interest and sustainability organisations, academics and other building practitioners.
>
> The ASBP champions the increased understanding and use of building products that meet demonstrably high standards of sustainability.
>
> For more information go to: **www.asbp.org.uk**

Where hazardous materials are being specified, alternatives with a lower environmental impact should be sought where possible.

Responsible sourcing considers the people involved in the abstraction or manufacture of the material or product. It is important to ensure that the human rights of these people are not being infringed through age, discrimination, welfare and working conditions.

When buying material made from natural resources such as timber it is important to ensure it is from a sustainable source. FSC or PEFC certified timber ensures a CoC from tree to site and that the timber is sustainably sourced.

Timber

To maintain the CoC both schemes require seven key pieces of information are displayed on the delivery tickets:

1   Supplier identification (name and address of the certified supplier providing the timber or timber products, ie the company name).

Figure 4.41   FSC-approved timber (courtesy Skanska)

2   Delivery address – usually the project with the main contractor's name.

3   Product identification (ie SW linings, OSB sheets, skirting).

4   Dimensional quantity of each product supplied and for BUILD UK member's volume (m³).

5   Date of delivery to site/document issue date.

6   Formal claim for each certified product (eg FSC 100 per cent, FSC X per cent, X per cent PEFC certified).

7   Proof of certification (the CoC number of the supplier, ie BMT-PEFC-1234).

If the timber is handled before it is delivered to a project and this person/ company does not hold CoC then they are breaking the chain. In this instance the timber should be delivered to the project from a supplier with chain or custody, or documentary evidence provided to trace the timber back to the source where the chain was broken.

> Timber from sustainable sources includes Greenpeace, Friends of the Earth, WWF, UK Forest and Trade Network UK.
>
> FSC retailers: **www.fsc-uk.org**
>
> UK Government Central Point of Expertise on Timber Procurement: **www.cpet.org.uk**

Aggregates and cement replacements

The use of recycled and secondary aggregates helps to reduce the demand for virgin quarried materials and can be a cost-effective alternative. Of the aggregates used in the UK each year, 70 million tonnes come from recycled or secondary sources. A good example is the use of pulverised fuel ash (PFA) or furnace bottom ash (FBA) as cement replacement in concrete. Other examples are detailed in Table 4.4.

Table 4.4   Examples of recycled and secondary sources of aggregate and cement replacements

Recycled	Secondary	
	Manufactured	*Natural*
• recycled aggregate (RA) • recycled concrete aggregate (RCA) • recycled asphalt • recycled asphalt planings (RAP) • spent rail ballast.	• blast furnace slag • steel slag • PFA • incinerator bottom ash (IBA) • FBA • used foundry sand • spent oil shale • recycled glass • recycled plastic • recycled tyres.	• slate aggregate • china clay sand • colliery spoil.

The Aggregates Levy (AGL) is an environmental tax that is levied on the commercial exploitation of rock, sand and gravel when used as aggregate for construction purposes. The purposes of the levy is to maximise the use of recycled aggregate and alternatives to virgin aggregate, and to promote the efficient use of virgin aggregate. The AGL is designed to encourage a shift in demand away from virgin aggregate towards recycled and secondary aggregates that can be produced on site through crushing (**Figure 4.42**) and screening (**Figure 4.43**).

Figure 4.42   On site crusher
               (courtesy Skanska)

Figure 4.43   Mobile screener
               (courtesy Galliford Try plc)

The importation, storage and placement of recycled and secondary aggregates on site requires an environmental permit, licence or exemption from the local environmental regulator at all times unless the aggregate has been produced in accordance with a quality protocol, for example the WRAP Quality Protocol for the production of aggregates from inert waste. The resultant aggregate in this example is classified as a recovered non-waste product.

WRAP have developed the Quality Protocol to help with the use of recycled aggregates in construction. In the context of construction and within clearly defined end uses, quality protocols for PFA, steel

For information about specifying, purchasing or supplying recycled or secondary aggregates go to: **http://aggregain.wrap.org.uk**

slag, IBA, tyre derived rubber materials and tyre bales are being considered. If recycled aggregates are sourced from a supplier, and accompanied by a quality certificate and test certificates, it should have ceased to be waste and does not need to be treated as such, unless it is subsequently discarded as waste.

On-site crushing and reuse of site-won inert materials (courtesy Kier)

4.7

Background

On-site crushing of inert materials, arising from demolition work, to produce fill for use on site, normally requires both space and large quantities of material for it to be feasible. However, the introduction of mini crushers has now made this operation practicable on small and constrained sites, as was demonstrated on the contract to refurbish Central Square at the University of East Anglia (UEA).

Central Square is the main public circulation area, and was fully renovated in 2009. This necessitated the removal of over 1200 m² of paving slabs. By careful handling, the site team managed to salvage nearly a third of these, handing them over to the UEA Estates Department for use in repairing other areas of existing paving across the campus.

The remaining slabs and concrete bed were crushed on site, over a period of four days, using a mini-crusher. This produced 260 tonnes of clean fill material that, following testing, was later reused in the works. The result was zero waste to landfill and a significant cost saving. Crushing the concrete on site also reduced the number of vehicle movements and the carbon emissions, on what was a very restricted site.

Costs and savings
- total cost of crusher, JCB and attendance: £1600 (£400/per day)
- potential cost of disposal: £1560 (260 tonnes of concrete at £6/t)
- cost of purchasing new material: £3120 (260 tonnes of concrete at £12/t)
- total saving to the project: £3080 (£3120 + £1560 – £1600).

Carbon emissions comparison
- offsite disposal, using a 20t lorry, would require thirteen 40 mile round trips, fuel used, at 8.5 mpg, would be $(40/8.5) \times 13 \times 4.546 = 278$ litres
- crusher, over four days at four litres of fuel per hour, used $4 \times 8 \times 4 = 128$ litres. Fuel saved 150 litres, which is equal to 390 kg of CO_2 (150×2.6 kg CO_2/l)
- for a crusher of this size, as dust suppression equipment was fitted and it was only on site for a short period, no environmental permit was required.

Use of recycled aggregate on the A3 Hindhead Road Tunnel project (courtesy Balfour Beatty)

Background

The A3 Hindhead Road Tunnel project was an important road improvement scheme to tackle congestion and safety issues, and improve the environment on this busy road. The project comprised a 6.5 km dual two-lane carriageway between Hammer Lane on the Surrey-Hampshire boundary and Boundless Lane near Thursley. Twin bored tunnels take the A3 under a SSSI adjacent to the Devil's Punchbowl.

Material used

Glass sand is a recycled aggregate made from glass bottles and jars, which can be used in the construction industry as a replacement for quarried or marine sand. Glass sand is made by crushing and screening glass waste to a particle size of 6 mm. Glass sand was used on the A3 in the following ways:

- constituent of cement bound material (CBM) used in the construction of the lower road base for the new A3 (up to 40 per cent)
- filter or protective layer lining all the scheme permanent infiltration and attenuation ponds for highways drainage
- filter layer in the scheme permanent soakaways for highways drainage from the new A3
- protective layer underlying the green roof for the tunnel service buildings.

Rationale for use

The potential for using glass sand on the A3 project was identified early in the construction phase and the majority was supplied by Viridor. The Highways Agency specification allowed for use of up to 40 per cent glass in the road base. The choice of recycled glass sand was made easier because there are no quarries near to the A3 project (30 mile radius) that can provide sand of a suitable quality. Neither was the Hythe sands excavated during earthworks work for the A3 earthworks fit for this purpose. The particle size of the glass sand makes it suitable for use as a filter and protective layer.

Economic and environmental benefits

- reduced the demand for sand or other primary aggregates that have to be quarried or dredged from estuaries
- reuse of glass reduces the volume of waste taken to landfill
- glass sand is an inert material and does not present a pollution risk
- reduced waste materials by producing CBM on-site
- cost savings of £191 235 compared to quarried sand
- on-site manufacture of CBM reduced potential delays from off-site production and delivery
- supply of the glass sand represents a cost saving to Viridor who would have to landfill the glass sand if they could not find an alternative use for the material
- use of recycled glass sand is economical, environmentally friendly, and its use is technically feasible and provides suitable quality and performance
- close liaison between the contractor, designer and client allowed for appropriate and effective use of recycled glass sand on the A3 project.

Plasterboard and gypsum

New plasterboard should be stored flat, undercover and away from traffic and moisture to prevent damage to the boards resulting in it becoming waste. It is unlikely that waste plasterboard generated during demolition or refit can be recycled due to contamination and this should be segregated from general waste to reduce disposal costs.

To reduce disposal costs construction projects should recycle plasterboard/gypsum waste where possible by arranging a take back scheme with the supplier. If a take back scheme is not possible then it should be separated for recovery and recycling with a certified waste contractor.

Plasterboard and gypsum waste that cannot be recovered or recycled should be sent to landfill. There are currently relatively few landfills that can accept such waste, so this disposal route is likely to lead to higher costs.

Non-hazardous gypsum-based and other high sulphate bearing materials should be deposited in landfills for non-hazardous waste in cells where no biodegradable waste is accepted. Any gypsum based materials classified as hazardous waste must be disposed of in a hazardous landfill.

Polyvinyl chloride (PVC)

The construction industry is one of the largest consumers of PVC, using it extensively in applications such as piping, cladding, wiring, flooring, windows and many others. It is estimated that the industry consumes in the region of 500 000 tonnes per annum. The issues surrounding PVC are contentious because of the many substances used during PVC manufacture and their release during accidental fire or incineration. Alternatives to PVC should be specified where possible.

Formaldehyde

Formaldehyde is most commonly used as a bonding material for composite boards such as medium density fibreboard (MDF) and plywood. Also, it is used in soft furnishings and carpets, providing a degree of fire retardation. Exposure to even low levels of formaldehyde through inhalation can cause irritation to the eyes, nose, throat, mucous membranes and skin. Unsealed chipboard, plywood, fire retardants and some furnishings have been found to yield measurable quantities of formaldehyde. In addition, when boards such as MDF are cut, a fine dust is created that can be respired leading to possible exposure to released formaldehyde. Formaldehyde-free and low formaldehyde containing boards and products are increasingly available in the UK and should be specified where possible.

Packaging

Packaging plays an important role in materials and product protection and ease of handling on site – too little increases product waste, too much increases packaging waste. Early engagement with the materials supplier will maximise opportunities to reduce the amount of waste material and packaging. Reductions can be found from the adoption of JIT deliveries and use of appropriately packaged goods for the site requirements.

Opportunities to reduce waste also exist through material and packaging recycling and take back schemes. Good segregation of used packaging materials will maximise these opportunities. Most suppliers will be subject to the legislative requirements and should be able to offer alternatives if excess package becomes waste on site.

4.5.2.4 Material assessment

When procuring materials, consideration needs to be given to client and legal requirements. Traditionally these have been referred to as:

- **preferred** – with reduced environmental or social impact (eg FSC timber)
- **advisory** – not banned, but those which clients would prefer not to be used (eg PVC)
- **prohibited** – banned by law (eg asbestos).

Following the update to BRE (1996) greater emphasis is being placed on Ecopoint scoring from A+ to E of main building elements, such as roof, floor or wall systems, rather that addressing materials in isolation. It is becoming increasingly common for specification lists to state an acceptable BRE Ecopoint band such as 'B' for a roofing system component, rather than to specify the avoidance of PVC. Where this is the case, liaison with the material manufacturer and reference to the BRE guide is necessary.

Increasingly a life cycle analysis (LCA) (or cradle to grave) approach is being taken to demonstrate the environmental impact or sustainability of products and materials. In Europe, the European Committee for Standardization (CEN) are undertaking several projects to standardise the environmental declarations of products.

The environmental impacts of materials selection are considered significant within the CEEQUAL and BREEAM assessment methodologies (see **Section 1.4**) and responsible sourcing of materials contributes to the overall score.

BRE Green Guide to Specification: **www.bre.co.uk/greenguide**

4.5.2.5 Material logistic planning

The use of logistics as a complementary approach to construction management is becoming more popular. Logistics are now a key feature of pre-construction planning, not only on large complex schemes, but also in the planning and delivery of mainstream housing and fit-out contracts. Material logistics planning not only encourages resource efficiency and reduces damage to materials, but also helps construction projects achieve programme certainty and cost predictability.

A materials logistics plan (MLP) sets out the following:

- types and quantities of materials to be used
- supply routes
- handling, storage, security arrangements
- use or installation
- reuse and disposal of any leftover materials.

WRAP RMP:
www.wrap.org.uk/content/resource-management-planning

WRAP BIM and resource efficiency:
www.wrap.org.uk/content/bim-and-resource-efficiency

WRAP MLP: www.wrap.org.uk/content/material-logistics-planning

A MLP can work alongside a RMP or a SWMP to ensure integrated, efficient management of the materials you buy and use on site.

4.5.2.6 Management of materials on site

Storing materials

The correct storage of materials is necessary to ensure they are:

- located at least 10 m away from sensitive receptors, eg watercourses, including drainage and transport routes, or more if there is no vegetated buffer zone
- unlikely to pollute: all potentially polluting materials should be stored in a designated area, on an impermeable base, bunded and away from potential vehicle collision
- not at risk of theft, vandalism or accidental damage
- not spoiled through exposure to the elements
- not subject to double handling – the more times materials are moved the more likely it is that damage will occur
- easily accessible
- on level ground to prevent damage from falling or toppling.

For guidance on effective storage of materials on site see the materials storage checklist in Section 4.5.2.7.

Managing materials

Different materials need to be managed in different ways according to their potential environmental impacts. For example, oil storage legislation require that oil containers are strong enough and that they are unlikely to burst or leak during ordinary use, containers must be within a drip tray, bund or other secondary containment system and must be located away from any watercourses (see Section 4.7.3) (in Scotland, this is only containers with a capacity over 200 litres).

The legislation does not apply in Wales, but consideration should be given to meeting such requirements, as they are designed to prevent contamination of the water environment that would be an offence under other legislation. Use the checklists provided in **Section 4.5.2.7** to ensure good practice with oil fuel storage and management.

Many materials that are potentially hazardous such as adhesives, solvents, paints and curing agents are regulated under the COSHH. Details of how these materials have to be stored, used and disposed of are stipulated in the COSHH datasheets, which should be followed. Copies of the datasheets and an inventory of all COSHH materials held on site should be

maintained. As a minimum all COSHH materials should be kept in a secure bunded COSHH store located away from drains and watercourses (**Figure 4.44**).

For all other materials, consider the appropriate means to handle products/materials to prevent them being damaged and becoming waste. For instance, store on pallets in designated areas and protected from the elements (eg wind and rain).

Figure 4.44   COSHH store sign (courtesy Laing O'Rourke)

Stockpiling

For any stockpile (**Figure 4.45**) that will be used on site for a long period, it is worth considering profiling and vegetating it to improve its stability and aesthetics (see **Section 4.5.2.7**), so as not to generate a nuisance from dust. Ensure control measures are in place to deal with silt runoff during wet conditions and dust during dry periods. Soil stockpiles or areas of exposed soil should be managed to prevent silty runoff from entering watercourses, drains, public highways and areas of the site where materials are stored. This can be done through bunding, vegetation, silt fencing and through the use of cut-off trenches, berms, bunds and covering (eg with hessian or jute matting).

Figure 4.45   Landscaped stockpile of spoil (courtesy Galliford Try plc)

Materials such as uncontaminated spoil arising from site set-up, sands and gravel excavations can be used to create a temporary bund or acoustic barrier while works are in progress and minimise silty

Consideration should be given to the need for an environmental permit, licence or waste management exemption.

runoff. Where the bund or barrier is situated needs careful consideration as does the need to comply with environmental permitting requirements.

Reuse of natural stone and other on-site recycling initiatives (courtesy Galliford Try plc)

Background

Construction of 120 m of natural stone clad reinforced concrete flood defence wall near to a small village hamlet. The site was located in a conservation area, which meant the wall had to be remade using existing stone on site or locally sourced-stone. An existing stone shed had to be dismantled and rebuilt as part of the works.

Material used

As part of the reconstruction of the wall about 300 m² of Natural York Stone walling was removed, cleaned, stored and reconstructed in exactly the same position and size without any damage being caused. This meant that no new materials had to be ordered or off site recycling undertaken. In addition the supporting wood beam from the stone shed was preserved and reused in the new structure.

Surplus excavated material was used to reinforce the existing flood bund. Undamaged pallets used to deliver bricks and other materials were registered with a pallet collection scheme and collected every month.

4.5.2.7 Good practice checklists

Materials procurement	
Substitute hazardous materials with non-hazardous alternatives	
Replace virgin materials (eg aggregates) with recycled products	
Order products with recycled content	
Source ethically-produced materials	
Order sustainably sourced materials, such as FSC timber or PEFC timber or procure products certified to the framework of BES 6001	
Consider the environmental impact of the material life cycle	
Consider transport distances of materials, ie are products sourced locally	

Resource efficiency	✓
Where appropriate reuse materials (eg aggregates) generated through on-site activity (eg temporary works or demolition/deconstruction)	
Make sure that when intending to reuse materials won on-site that they are suitable for the intended use and do not contain contaminants that could potentially cause pollution or hard to sensitive receptors	
If uncertain about the suitability of site won materials to be reused consult a specialist for advice	
Only order the required amount	
Order materials cut to size to reduce off-cuts	
Establish JIT systems, so that materials are not stored on site unnecessarily, reducing potential damage	
When deliveries arrive on site: • ensure they are off-loaded in a designated area of site • check good to ensure that they are the correct specification and quantity • do not accept delivery of damaged goods	
When handling materials, avoid damage or spillage through incorrect or repetitive handling	

Materials storage	✓
Identify mechanisms that allow for beneficial reuse and avoid materials becoming waste by using them on the next project	
Store all containers of potential polluting materials, such as oils and paints, in a bunded area	
Designate responsibility for hazardous materials storage, restrict and manage access	
Clearly mark storage area(s)	
Store materials in suitable containers that are labelled appropriately with fitted lids, taps and tops in good condition	
Put control measures in place and/or locate spill kits near to bulk stores and ensure they are accessible and fully stocked	
Store material so as to guard against breakage, vandalism or theft	
Protect stores against flood damage or inundation	
Store waste in a designated area away from the materials storage	

Managing stockpiles	✓	
Store topsoil for reuse in piles less than two metres high to prevent damage to the soil structure		
Segregate different grades of soil		
Position spoil and temporary stockpiles a minimum of 10 m away from watercourses and drainage systems		
Minimise movements of materials in stockpiles to reduce degradation of the soil structure		
Silty water formed by erosion of the stockpile should be managed correctly		
Direct surface water away from the stockpiles to prevent erosion at the bottom		
Place silt screens around spoil heaps to trap silt from any surface water runoff		
Vegetate long-term stockpiles to prevent dust in dry weather conditions, and reduce erosion of the stockpile to form silty runoff. Ensure adequate weed control		

Refuelling protocol	✓	
Designate a bunded refuelling area, away from site drains on an impermeable surface		
Avoid using remote fill points. Where these are unavoidable install suitable oil separators to the surface drainage system		
Avoid refuelling close to watercourses		
When refuelling keep materials such as absorbent pads or booms readily available in case of spillage		
All refuelling should be supervised. Do not leave valves open unattended (note that auto-close valves may be a legal requirement)		
Keep an emergency spill kit at each refuelling point. If mobile refuelling is carried out, ensure each bowser carries a spill kit		
Bowsers should have an automatic cut out and should be locked when not in use		
Ensure that site staff carrying out refuelling are aware of the protocol and know what actions to take in an emergency		

Storing, fuels and chemicals	✓	
Securely store all containers that contain potential pollutants (eg fuels, oils and chemicals) according to oil storage legislation		
Label containers clearly, so that appropriate remedial action can be taken in the event of a spillage		
All bulk fuel storage should be integrally bunded or kept within a bunded area		

Storing, fuels and chemicals	✓
Regularly check taps and hoses for leakage and signs of damage	
Avoid storing drums tightly against each other. Store drums so that they can all be inspected for leaks	
Prevent damage from vandalism. Ensure that all valves and trigger guns are vandal and tamper proof	
Display a notice that demands valves and trigger guns are to be locked when not in use	
Store tanks or drums in a secure bunded container or compound that is locked when not in use	
Fuel, oil and chemicals must be stored on an impermeable base (this may be part of a bund). Ideally, such materials should be stored away from areas of groundwater contamination risk. This should be identified in the contract but may be worth discussing with the environmental agencies	
Provide separate fill pipes for each tank unless the tanks are interconnected by a balance pipe of greater flow capacity than the fill pipe	
Mark fill pipes with the product type and a tank number where there is more than one tank	
Before moving a drum, check the bung is secure	

Bunding tanks	✓
To avoid accidental spillage, bund tanks with a minimum capacity of 110 per cent of the volume of the largest tank or 25 per cent of the total storage capacity, whichever is the greater	
Do not allow bunded areas to fill with rainwater or slops (ideally, provide a cover). Empty and dispose of any water collected in an appropriate way	
Site tanks away from vehicle movements and mark them clearly, so that people know they are a potential risk	
Do not put tanks where there is a direct link to surface drains, watercourses or sewers. Avoid placing tanks on unpaved ground, to reduce the risk of groundwater and soil contamination. Protect tanks from vandalism	
The bund should be impermeable to the substance that is being stored in the tank	
Position air vent pipes, so that they can be seen easily and directed so that any discharge (eg in the event of the tank being overfilled) is directed down into the bund	
Fill points must be inside the bund	
Fit any pumps sited outside the bund with a non-return/check valve installed in the feed line	

4.5.2.8 Further reading

WRAP (2004) *Quality protocol for the production of aggregates from inert waste*, The Waste and Resources Action Programme, Oxon, UK. Go to: **http://tinyurl.com/nr6k9xh**

WRAP (2013) *Aggregates from inert waste. End of waste criteria for the production of aggregates from inert waste*, The Waste and Resources Action Programme, Oxon, UK. Go to: **http://tinyurl.com/pzcfga6** (accessed 16 December 2014)

BS 8903:2010 *Principles and framework for procuring sustainably. Guide*

4.5.2.9 Legislation

Legislation is constantly changing, including amendments and new legislation, and this varies between England, Wales, Scotland and Northern Ireland. If site staff are unsure on any environmental issue, contact the regional environmental regulator for advice.

Legislation	Key requirements	Applicable Nation(s)
Timber and Timber Products (Placing on the Market) Regulations 2013	This counters the trade in illegally harvested timber and timber products through three key obligations: • it prohibits the placing on the EU market for the first time of illegally harvested timber and products derived from such timber • it requires EU traders who place timber products on the EU market for the first time to exercise 'due diligence' • it requires operators to keep records of their suppliers and customers for five years.	England, Wales, Scotland, Northern Ireland
The Registration, Evaluation, Authorisation and Restriction of Chemicals (REACH) Enforcement Regulations 2008 (as amended)	If chemicals are used on site that are not common check with the supplier to see if they comply with the REACH regulations. Safety data sheets should be provided with each chemical kept on site: these will be provided by the supplier. All safety data sheets should be kept with the appropriate chemical. The recommended risk assessments should be checked for feasibility on the site for storage and use. If the risk assessment is not adequate for use on site a new risk assessment should be carried out and documented.	England, Wales, Scotland, Northern Ireland
Water Environment (Oil Storage) (Scotland) Regulations 2006	Where oil is stored in any portable container with a storage capacity of less than 200 litres, the container must be of sufficient strength and structural integrity to ensure that it is unlikely to burst or leak in its ordinary use. Where the container has a storage capacity of 200 litres or more, the Regulations require provision of a secondary containment (a bund or drip-tray) to ensure that any leaking or spilt oil cannot enter the water environment.	Scotland

Legislation	Key requirements	Applicable Nation(s)
Control of Substances Hazardous to Health Regulations 2002 (as amended) Control of Substances Hazardous to Health Regulations (Northern Ireland) 2003 (as amended)	The organisation: • shall ensure that the exposure of its employees to substances hazardous to health is either prevented or, where this is not reasonably practicable, adequately controlled • providing any control measure, personal protective equipment (PPE) or facility pursuant to these Regulations shall take all reasonable steps to ensure that it is properly used or applied as specified • providing any control measure shall ensure that it is maintained in an efficient state, in efficient working order and in good repair. PPE should be in a clean condition • shall ensure that employees who are or are liable to be exposed to a hazardous substance are under suitable health surveillance • shall prepare procedures, provide information and establish warning systems to deal with an emergency in the workplace related to the presence of a substance hazardous to health.	England, Wales, Scotland, Northern Ireland
The Aggregates Levy (General) Regulations 2002 (as amended)	A tax placed on sand, gravel and rock extracted from the ground or dredged from the sea to encourage an increase in the use of recycled materials.	England, Wales, Scotland, Northern Ireland
Control of Pollution (Oil Storage) (England) Regulations 2001 Control of Pollution (Oil Storage) (Northern Ireland) Regulations 2010 (as amended)	Imposes general requirements for preventing pollution of controlled waters from oil storage, particularly fixed tanks, drums or mobile bowsers. The legislation applies to the storage of 200 litres or more of oil of any kind, including petrol, but excluding the storage of waste oil. Restrictions also govern the use of pumps. It details requirements for oil stored in tanks, drums, mobile browsers or underground that must be identified and implemented, and makes contravention a criminal offence.	England, Northern Ireland

4.5.3 Waste

4.5.3.1 Introduction

In England and Wales the construction and demolition industry is responsible for generating up to 77.4 million tonnes of construction, demolition and excavation waste per year and approximately 19.8 million tonnes of this total is sent to landfill (Defra, 2012. Note these figures are as of 2010). The total amount of waste generated equates to about one-third of all waste produced in a year in England and Wales, and makes up around half of all controlled waste in Scotland. The industry is the third largest producer of hazardous waste.

Waste not only significantly affects the environment, but handling waste inefficiently will cost time, money and effort. For example, by not segregating waste initially, inert material may have to be disposed of as non-hazardous or hazardous waste, depending on the waste it is mixed with, which is more expensive and stops the reuse of the waste. Often people think that waste costs are related only to its disposal. In fact, the true cost of waste is eight to 10 times the disposal cost and includes:

- purchase price of materials that are being wasted
- cost of storage, transport and disposal of excess materials/waste
- cost of the time spent managing and handling the waste
- loss of income from not reusing waste materials.

4.5.3.2 Waste impacts

The environmental impacts of waste are many and wide ranging, but can be divided into two main categories:

1 **Direct impacts**

   a **emissions** – any processing of waste before disposal (on or off site) requires energy, so contributes to emissions to atmosphere

   b **energy emissions from transport** – each load of waste removed from site is responsible for transport emissions to the atmosphere

   c **landfill emissions** – as waste undergoes chemical, physical and biological change in landfill it releases emissions to the atmosphere, such as CO_2 and methane, that then affects air quality and contributes to emissions into the atmosphere of GHGs

   d **land use** – disposal to landfill requires the use and contamination of land that takes away a commodity that could be used for more beneficial purposes, or simply left for ecological value.

2 **Indirect impacts**

   a impacts of raw material use and energy consumption in production of product, material, packaging etc before becoming a waste

   b recycling uses energy, produces emission pollutions and generates waste

   c landfill as contaminated land requires extensive clean up or remediation before it can be reused

   d energy use and emissions as a consequence of transport, processing and disposal of waste following transfer of waste to new holder.

The effects of waste at regional and national levels are wide ranging and collectively there is a major impact on the environment. Waste is considered as one of the most important environmental issues to manage properly.

Figure 4.46   Site recycling (courtesy SEPA)

There are two principles of sustainably managing waste:

1   **Resource efficiency** – reducing the generation of waste in the first place.

2   **Effective waste management** – diverting remaining waste from landfill into reuse, recycle and recovery (see **Section 4.5.3.6**).

These principles are acted upon through several mechanisms in the UK construction industry, from European Directives through to national legislation.

Legislation as it applies to a construction site can be summarised as having two principle aims in the industry:

1   To ensure the disposal of waste is regulated (and traceable).

2   To ensure that the cost of waste disposal is borne by the waste producer, in-line with the polluter pays principle (PPP).

To meet the wider aims eliminating waste and diverting waste from landfill there are many strategies in place that are highlighted in **Section 4.5.3.4**.

4.5.3.3   Definition of different types of waste

The European Waste Catalogue (EWC) can be used to identify waste and assigns a six digit code to it that helps to determine how waste can be disposed. These six digit codes are required to be written on waste transfer evidence (see **Case study 4.15**). For the purposes of landfill disposal, wastes can be divided into the following:

- **inert waste** includes rocks, ceramics, concrete, masonry and brick rubble

- **non-hazardous waste** is non-contaminated biodegradable materials, including paper, cardboard, plastic, metal, timber, topsoil and food

- **hazardous/special (Scotland) waste** is contaminated and harmful materials and deemed to be dangerous to life and/or damaging to the environment.

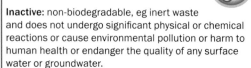

The terms active and inactive may also be used along with hazardous, non-hazardous and inert category classifications, defined as:

Inactive: non-biodegradable, eg inert waste and does not undergo significant physical or chemical reactions or cause environmental pollution or harm to human health or endanger the quality of any surface water or groundwater.

Active: biodegradable, eg wood, plastics, food, topsoil, which break down and undergo significant physical and chemical reactions. They may cause environmental pollution or harm to human health or endanger the quality of any surface water or groundwater.

Hazardous wastes may be corrosive, explosive, oxidising, carcinogenic or flammable. Examples include asbestos, acids, alkaline solutions, oily sludges, waste oils and wood preservatives.

4.5.3.4 Waste management initiatives

Circular economy

The Ellen MacArthur Foundation set out the principles of a circular economy in two business-focused annual reports (started in 2012). These reports suggest that a step-change is needed in how resources

Ellen MacArthur Foundation:
www.ellenmacarthurfoundation.org

Circular Economy 100:
**www.ellenmacarthurfoundation.
org/business/ce100**

are sourced and managed. They advocate a systems approach, where the whole business cycle uses and reuses resources more efficiently, eliminating waste and instead using all by-products. The Circular Economy 100 is a global group of leading businesses, including contractors and clients, who collaborate to encourage the transition to a circular economy.

Resource efficiency

Resource efficiency is the next step on from waste reduction, and is becoming widely accepted as the driving concept in waste and resource management. Encouraged by government, and organisations such as WRAP and BRE, resource efficiency focuses on making the most of resources to gain maximum cost benefit and minimise environmental impact.

National strategies/local authorities

Each of the UK regions and some local authorities have developed and published their own strategies for waste management by setting targets and developing process to reduce the amount of waste produced.

Community schemes

There are a number of local community schemes that promote waste management. The aim of these schemes is to collate information on the local community waste schemes available.

Others aim to provide waste management solutions, usually run by social enterprises, for local businesses and/or works. An example is the Community Wood Recycling project providing options for wood and timber recycling and also locations for purchasing recycled timber products.

Background

4.10

At the Bidston Moss Viaduct site a bailing machine was used to create plastic bales from shrink wrap and polythene previously used for containment. The baler took five skips worth of plastic to produce one bale weighing one tonne and paid back its £10 000 cost in three months. It was estimated to save the project twice the cost and the project team had the baler as an asset at the end of the project. More importantly, 452 vehicle movements were eliminated reducing the impact on the environment and local community. All the plastic bales were then collected and recycled.

Lessons learnt

This is a good example of the use of innovative technologies to reduce construction waste and impact.

4.5.3.5 Waste management on site

To effectively manage waste on site, a standard approach should be adopted as follows:

1   Planning.

2   Managing.

3   Monitoring.

4   Reporting.

These collectively combine good practice techniques and legislation and is reflected in this section of the guide.

Figure 4.47 outlines the activities to apply waste management on site. The following section explains this process in more detail.

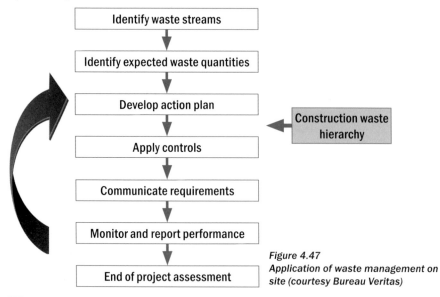

Figure 4.47
Application of waste management on site (courtesy Bureau Veritas)

Planning

A RMP or a SWMP is useful tool for managing waste on site. A SWMP in particular may be required under the planning permission, by the client or main contractor, or to obtain BREEAM points. SWMP are generally considered good practice.

Site waste management planning should have the involvement of all parts of the project team, including the client, contractors, designers and workers, not based on site. It is useful to identify one site-based employee from the main/principal contractor to be responsible for the development and implementation of the SWMP or processes. This individual should have sufficient knowledge and experience of the project processes and enough influence within the project team to ensure that the site waste management planning is effective.

Before work begins it is necessary to plan for waste management. This should include ways of minimising waste arisings, materials and waste storage, and logistics such as take-back schemes. Many product suppliers offer these schemes to take back packaging and/or left over product reducing unnecessary waste on site.

Client and designers role in planning for waste management

The client should be involved in the planning stage. However, the most beneficial waste reduction opportunities should be identified by members of the design team, which may include engineers, architects and quantity surveyors. This is often referred to as 'designing out waste', and should contribute to the projects resource efficiency.

Engaging the client and designers will help ensure that waste reduction decisions and actions are achievable and agreed by all who are involved in the project delivery. Many of the most effective methods to reduce waste are achieved through design and specifications on projects. It is good practice for the client and principle contractor to sign a joint declaration of commitment to the SWMP.

Earthworks planning

For earthworks it is worth considering the CL:AIRE CoP (2011). This document sets out an auditable good practice methodology that can be applied for assessing whether or not materials are classified as waste and for determining when treated waste can cease to be waste for a particular use. This will help to identify whether or not an environmental permit may be required. The CL:AIRE cluster guide (2012) sets out the 'cluster methodology' designed to offer an alternative way of developing and remediating multiple sites that are located relatively close by.

Segregation of recycling

Segregation of various recycling streams is often advisable where space allows and these include plastics, metals, glass, paper and card. Space for collection, segregation, storage and possibly treatment of waste (eg individual and/or communal bin stores, composting facilities, waste treatment facilities) should be allocated within the planning application site layout.

1

2

3

4

Appendices

Managing waste

Identify waste streams

WRAP Net Waste Tool: www.wrap.org.uk/content/net-waste-tool-0

Undertake a review of the project plans, programme, design etc to identify each type of waste that is expected to be produced, including identifying those that are inert (inactive), non-hazardous (active) and hazardous. If using a SWMP, record the expected wastes in it.

For each type of waste identified, estimate the quantities expected to be generated and associated cost of traditional disposal. This estimation should be based on previous experience, or industry averages. WRAP's Net Waste Tool can be used to forecast arisings as well as assess recycled content.

By identifying potential waste streams (types and quantities) that could arise during a construction project, there is a greater likelihood that these can be effectively managed and diverted from landfill.

For each waste stream identified consideration needs to be given as to how the waste will be disposed of, eg timber off-cuts, general waste skip, landfill.

The information gathered on waste streams and disposal routes is used to estimate the expected costs for waste disposal. This is the cost expected to pay for wastes identified if no improvements are made to the disposal options, eg material x skip hire x transfer fees x disposal cost x no. of skips = £xxx.

Develop waste action plan

Using the principles of the waste hierarchy (**Figure 4.50**) a plan should be developed for each waste stream identified. Opportunities for each stage of the hierarchy should be considered and the most suitable (practical, financial, technical) option selected. This plan should demonstrate both reductions in overall waste expected to be generated and the reductions in waste to be sent to landfill.

To develop suitable actions it is important that the client and architect and/or designers are involved in the process. In some contracts this may require subcontractors input. Examples include:

* developing standardised sizes or pre-cut materials to reduce off cuts (eg timber)
* negotiating take-back schemes with suppliers
* identifying opportunities to reuse materials between trades
* providing storage areas for materials to be reused on site
* specifying/negotiating reduction in the amount of packaging used by suppliers, or packaging return schemes
* specifying pre-cast units (eg concrete panels rather than on-site pours).

Each waste stream in the action plan should have a corresponding action (some may require more than one action) to reduce waste. These can be used to monitor progress in reducing waste.

> Waste management should start with resource efficiency by using the raw materials procured more wisely. To manage wastes effectively, focus on ways to prevent materials becoming waste.

It is good practice to record the waste action plan within the SWMP document for the site. The SWMP should include details of disposal methods for waste on the project, for instance waste carriers and waste disposal facilities (as included within SWMP templates developed by WRAP). At the time of planning it is important to take into account the availability of facilities in the area of the site.

At this stage ensure to obtain copies of environmental permits/licenses for each of the waste streams identified.

> WRAP SWMP templates:
> **http://tinyurl.com/mdgbpps**

Storing and treating waste

During construction if waste material is to be stored on site before collection and treatment or treated on site (eg crushing or reusing) then, depending on the national environmental regulator, an environmental permit, license, Pollution Prevention and Control (PPC) permit or exemption could be required, resulting in extra costs to the project. For example, using baling equipment to reduce the volume of waste may require an exemption. If there is an exemption in place, it must comply with the conditions set out in it.

Waste management during contaminated land remediation (courtesy Galliford Try plc)

One of the largest tyre dumps in Europe was remediated using tyre stabilisation and capping techniques. The first stage involved re-profiling the remaining tyres into a regular shape and covering them. The second stage involved the construction of a specifically designed cover, which comprised a layer of geogrid membrane, a layer of inert waste shale from a local source and completed with a layer of local limestone.

Details of materials reused on the project to reduce the amount of waste generated included:

- use of 19 000 tonnes of waste shale and limestone dust in the engineering cap, which would have gone to landfill. This material was acquired through the procurement system and resulted in a landfill tax saving of £455 000, more than the actual project value

- concrete slabs that were already present on site were used as temporary security fencing/road blocks during the scheme and then made into a permanent fence on project completion

- mature trees taken down to make way for the engineering cap were made into log sections and stored on site. On completion of the cap they were then redistributed around the site in log piles to provide new habitat for hibernating mammals, reptiles and ground nesting birds

- limestone blocks already *in situ* were used for habitat provision. These latter two initiatives were not part of the original design, but provided added value to the scheme by encouraging new habitat to flourish on the site, which had previously been an eyesore and a drain on local resources.

Obtain guidance from the environmental regulator before undertaking any storing or treating of waste on site.

Once the waste has been suitably treated on site in accordance with the waste permit, licence or exemption and it fulfils the WRAP Quality Protocol, it may no longer be classed as a waste and can be used for its defined purpose on site.

Figure 4.48   Segregated skips (courtesy BAM Nuttall)

Apply controls

Having defined the site waste management arrangements (such as a SWMP) and action plan, apply controls on site to ensure that the plans are achieved, which starts with defining facilities.

Define facilities on site

Ensure that sufficient space is allocated on site for the waste expected. This should include the transfer of waste from remote locations to a central waste area. Clearly mark these areas on site plans for communication purposes. When waste is being stored on site it is important that the storage areas have clear signage to ensure different wastes are stored in the correct place.

Before stockpiling wastes on site for reuse or recycling, identify where the material is going to be used. If there is no space on site to segregate wastes for reuse or recycling, consider off-site recycling by using a waste management contractor that has the necessary facilities. Consider the use of reused and recycled materials on site. To find sources of such materials talk to local demolition contractors and local authority recycling officers.

The storage provided should be:

● on a hard standing area away from drains and watercourses

● clearly marked, eg use waste aware signs

● enclosed/secured to prevent waste escaping, eg blown by wind or from unauthorised access

● segregated by type where possible

● engineered to contain that waste type, ie to prevent escape, including leaking of liquids.

In addition:

● hazardous wastes must not be mixed

● hazardous wastes must be stored in suitable containment.

Dedicated hazardous waste storage area (courtesy Parsons Brinckerhoff)

Issue

At the Hutton Substation in Cumbria, hazardous waste storage was not on an impermeable base, was difficult to access, located outside and uncovered causing build-up of rainwater in bunds.

Lessons learnt

A dedicated hazardous waste storage area was set up within a waterproof shelter on a concrete base. Oil drums were provided with an appropriate drum spill pallet. Access was such that plant could be used to move drums/containers, removing the requirement for manual handling. All hazardous waste was clearly labelled with consistent signage that included the EWC codes. Where possible, such an area for hazardous waste should be included in the planning stages of a project and put in place at site mobilisation.

Figure 4.49   Dedicated hazardous waste storage area (courtesy J Murphy and Sons Ltd)

If it is intended to use a material recovery facility (MRF) to sort and recycle waste, it will be necessary to discuss the on-site facility requirements with the contractor to ensure that the best results are achieved. This will include establishing exactly what can be placed in a general waste skip without contaminating the waste and preventing it being recovered and recycled.

Communicate

As each site will have different requirements for waste management, it is important that these requirements are communicated to relevant parties (ie site-based staff and subcontractors).

All site-based staff should be made aware of the waste management requirements at induction as a minimum. It is good practice for the principal contractor to make the SWMP available to all contractors carrying out work on their behalf, and that these contractors know where the SWMP is held.

Site induction

Ensure that the site specific requirements for waste (including relevant action plans) are included in the site induction, and provided to all who work on site. This does not need to be the full details of the plan, but just those areas relevant to their activities.

Monitoring and reporting performance

Updating the site waste management planning

It is considered good practice to update the waste management records or SWMP each time waste is removed from site or at least on a monthly basis, with the waste transfer evidence/consignment note information. Following this procedure provides a useful check that the transfer notes are being completed correctly and ensures records are up-to-date at all times.

A thorough review of the waste management records or SWMP should be carried out monthly, to assess performance against the waste action plan and targets. The review should include calculating the costs of waste treatment and disposal.

The site manager should allocate responsibility to a nominated person to carry out waste audits/inspections at regular intervals to look at:

- quantities of each type of waste generated, reasons why and its cost implications
- how wastes are being handled and stored
- recommendations for improving waste management.

Carrying out audits will provide valuable information to help set targets for improvement and will show how well waste management initiatives from the action plan are working on site.

MRF monitoring

Where possible, it is good practice to ensure that exact recovery and recycling data from MRF's is obtained rather than average statistics, which will not accurately reflect the sites performance.

End of project assessment

At the completion of the project, it is good practice for the person responsible for waste management on site to undertake a full review of the plan and document expected performance, ie action plan, against the actual performance achieved. This review should include a comparison of the expected waste management costs versus actual waste costs.

This review will provide valuable information internally that can be used on future projects to define site waste management planning and assist in development of SWMP for other projects, and compare performance.

4.5.3.6 Waste hierarchy

Legislation states that waste management priorities and practical actions on site must follow the principles of the waste hierarchy (**Figure 4.50**). A declaration that this has been applied to the waste should be included on the relevant duty of care documentation (see **Section 4.5.3.8**).

4.5.3.7 Waste disposal

Any waste disposed of to landfill sites is subject to landfill tax. Landfill tax is regulated by HMRC and is designed to encourage businesses to produce less waste and to use alternative forms of waste management/disposal. It is a levy charged by weight and there are two rates for inert (inactive) and non-hazardous (active) waste. Inert (inactive) waste is charged at a substantially lower rate than non-hazardous (active) waste. If these waste types are mixed together the higher rate of tax will be charged on the whole load, so segregating waste saves money.

Waste arising from the following activities is exempt, subject to meeting certain conditions:

- some dredging activities
- quarrying and mining
- reclamation of contaminated land.

The cost of landfill tax for non-hazardous (active) wastes is £80 per tonne at April 2014. The rate will not fall below £80 per tonne between 2014/2015 to 2019/2020. Inert (inactive) wastes are charged at a lower cost for £2.50 per tonne.

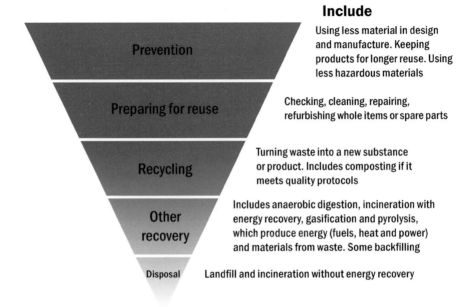

Include

Using less material in design and manufacture. Keeping products for longer reuse. Using less hazardous materials

Checking, cleaning, repairing, refurbishing whole items or spare parts

Turning waste into a new substance or product. Includes composting if it meets quality protocols

Includes anaerobic digestion, incineration with energy recovery, gasification and pyrolysis, which produce energy (fuels, heat and power) and materials from waste. Some backfilling

Landfill and incineration without energy recovery

Figure 4.50   Waste hierarchy

4.5.3.8 Duty of care

There is a duty of care to ensure that waste is dealt with appropriately. The person on site with responsibility for waste management must be able to describe both the waste kept on site and the waste transported off site.

> Green taxes, reliefs and schemes for businesses:
> **www.gov.uk/green-taxes-and-reliefs/landfill-tax**

Disposal of waste from site must only be carried out by a registered waste carrier who should be able to provide a colour copy of their waste carriers' certificate. Details of the certificate can be checked with the environmental regulator. If an organisation carries its own waste, legislation requires it to register as a waste carrier. Waste should only be accepted at a site that is either permitted/licensed or exempt as appropriate.

Using a SWMP and carefully recording waste movements to and from site can help assure that the duty of care requirements are met.

Environmental permitting/licensing

In England and Wales, legislation requires 'waste operations' to hold an environmental permit or have an exemption. Waste operations mean any recovery (including storage pending recycling/reclamation etc) or disposal of waste that requires an environmental permit, unless the waste operation is specifically exempt or excluded under the legislation.

In Northern Ireland and Scotland waste operations will be authorised by a waste management licence, an exemption from waste management licensing or a PPC permit, depending on the nature of the waste management activity.

For all countries in the UK, it is important to identify whether an environmental permit or licence is required for operations carried out on or off site.

> A recycling company was ordered to pay a record £200 000 penalty for dumping tonnes of construction and demolition waste at the former Woodend Colliery in Armadale, West Lothian, without a licence.

Waste transfer evidence/notes (inert and non-hazardous waste)

All inert and non-hazardous waste leaving the site must be accompanied by waste transfer evidence (England and Wales) or a note (WTN) (Scotland and Northern Ireland), which needs to include the following information for controlled waste:

- description of the waste
- List of Wastes (LoW) or EWC code
- how it is contained
- quantity of waste
- the place, date and time of transfer
- the name and address of both parties (ie carrier and holder/producer) – site and either transfer or end disposal as applicable
- details of the permit, licence or exemption of the person receiving the waste
- declaration that the waste hierarchy has been applied (England, Wales and Northern Ireland only)
- Standard Industrial Classification (SIC) code (2007)
- signatures of both parties (transferor and transferee).

Copies of waste transfer evidence needs to be kept by the waste producer, the waste carrier, waste broker (if applicable) and the waste disposer. These records need to be kept for a minimum of two years.

The transfer note records the transfer of waste between two parties. It does not record the full journey of the waste and there is no requirement to write the site of final disposal or recovery unless that is where the transfer takes place. However, companies are required to take action that is reasonable to confirm their waste has been managed legally once it leaves their site. Many companies choose to follow waste from their site to confirm it has been taken to an exemption, permitted or licensed waste management facility for treatment or disposal.

An electronic alternative to the existing paper-based system of waste transfer evidence and notes is also available. The electronic duty of care (EDOC) programme is a national, internet-based system to monitor the collection, transportation and disposal of waste materials. It is designed to, make it easier for businesses and regulators to collect, collate and extract good quality waste transfer data.

Completing and checking waste transfer evidence (courtesy Laing O'Rourke)

Waste must be transported in accordance with the Waste (England and Wales) (Amendment) Regulations 2014. All construction and demolition waste must be transported by a waste carrier that is registered with the environmental regulator and waste transfer evidence must be completed for every load of waste removed. The Regulations also state that copies of all waste transfer evidence should be kept for at least two years.

4.14

In most cases, waste transfer evidence will be completed and provided by the waste contractor. However, it is the responsibility of the producer/holder of the waste to ensure that the information on these documents is accurate and correct before it is signed. If an organisation needs to complete its own waste transfer evidence or Hazardous Waste Consignment Note (HWCN), contact the procurement department to order waste documentation pads. Templates are available if needed. Also note that three copies of each document may be required (for the producer, carrier and disposer).

Waste transfer evidence must contain the following information:

- a description of the waste including the EWC Code
- description of how the waste is contained, eg 7 yd skip, 200 ltr drums, loose
- quantity of the waste (the weight or volume)
- address and postcode from which the waste is being removed
- address and postcode to which the waste is being taken
- permit number or exemption reference for the site to which the waste is being taken
- SIC code
- waste carrier's vehicle registration number
- waste carrier registration number
- application of the waste hierarchy declaration ("I confirm that I have fulfilled my duty to apply the waste hierarchy as required by Regulation 12 of the Waste Regulations 2014")
- date and time of collection
- transferor's signature
- driver's signature (as the transferee).

Annual waste transfer evidence

Annual waste transfer evidence (also known as a season ticket) can be used for repeat transfers. This is a single evidence document or note that can cover multiple transfers over a period of up to 12 months. Using a season ticket can be agreed if all of the following conditions remain the same:

- the waste producer, the waste carrier and the waste destination
- the description and type of waste being transferred
- the site where the waste comes from.

If any of these conditions change, a new evidence document or note will be required. Contact the waste contractor for more information if an annual waste transfer evidence for waste on the site can be used.

Consignment notes – hazardous/special waste

All hazardous/special waste leaving the site must be accompanied by a consignment note that travels with the waste to its final treatment or disposal option. Information that must be recorded on the consignment note includes:

- waste producer
- waste carrier
- premises code
- description of waste
- LoW/EWC code
- quantity (kg)
- chemical/biological components of waste and their concentrations
- physical form
- hazardous code(s)
- container type, number and size
- declaration that the waste hierarchy has been applied (England, Wales and Northern Ireland only)
- SIC code (2007) (England, Wales and Northern Ireland only).

> Electronic Duty of Care (EDOC):
> **www.edoconline.co.uk**

> A company and one of its directors pleaded guilty after an Environment Agency investigation revealed a disused railway cutting was being illegally filled with waste from a construction project at the company's site at East Grinstead. The company was fined £15 000 and ordered to pay costs of £2315, while its director was fined £2000.

Copies of the consignment note need to be kept by the producer for at least three years.

In England and Wales the consignee (the person whom waste is transferred to for recovery or disposal) issues records to the site (consignor) of the waste disposed, including copies of consignment note and information on waste received, disposed, or recovery of waste (known as quarterly returns). These returns must be retained by the holder at the registered site, or registered office after the site closes.

To move hazardous waste in Northern Ireland pre-notification is required and a uniquely coded consignment note must be obtained from the NIEA. There is a small fee and the note is required even if transporting directly to England, Wales or Scotland. Notification is required before movement can proceed.

The consignment note is uniquely coded. In Scotland, all special waste movements are required to be pre-notified to SEPA via a special waste consignment note.

Hazardous waste must be transported in accordance with Hazardous Waste (England and Wales) Regulations 2005 as amended. All hazardous waste must be transported by a waste carrier that is registered with the environmental regulator and a HWCN must be completed for every load of hazardous waste removed and retained for at least three years after the deposit of the waste.

It is the consignor's responsibility to complete Parts A, B and D of the HWCN. If the waste contractor completes Parts A and B, the information provided must be checked to ensure that it is accurate. The carrier will complete Part C upon inspecting the waste. It is the consignee's responsibility to complete Part E and return a copy of this to the consignor within three months of receiving the waste. This provides confirmation that the waste has been received by the consignee and also how it has been treated or disposed of.

Note: the consignee is also required to submit hazardous waste returns to the Environment Agency every quarter.

If hazardous waste is being stored on site, even for a short period of time, then:

- ensure that it is stored safely and securely to prevent pollution
- ensure that it is packaged and labelled correctly
- keep different types of hazardous waste separate
- keep hazardous and non-hazardous waste separate
- keep liquid hazardous waste in a dedicated area, with a bund or barrier to contain spills and leaks
- regularly check storage areas for leaks, deteriorating containers or other potential risks
- display written instructions for storing and disposing of each type of hazardous waste
- maintain an inventory of the hazardous wastes kept on the premises, and where they are stored – this will help the emergency services to deal with any incident effectively and safely.

Wastes requiring specialist services

Certain wastes require specialists to remove and dispose of them when they are found on site, for example asbestos and sharps (see the following sections). Removal of asbestos or sharps must be carried out under a specific method statement (MS) that has been reviewed and approved by the contractor.

Asbestos

Asbestos is a hazardous material that in the past was extensively used in various applications including:

- insulation of pipes and boilers
- fire protection in panels, wall partitions, ceiling panels and around structural steel work
- roof and wall cladding
- gutters, rainwater pipes and water tanks
- reinforced plastics and sealants
- bound in concrete.

During renovation or demolition the asbestos may be disturbed through drilling, cutting or sanding. Such disturbance releases potentially harmful fibres into the atmosphere that could cause serious health problems. If asbestos is found or suspected, stop work immediately and contact a specialist contractor to remove it. Specialist licences for transport and disposal are required for asbestos wastes.

> One example of an on-site activity requiring careful management is that of road sweeper arisings generated by keeping site access routes clean. These arisings could contain fuel residues, road salt and other substances that may harm the environment. As part of the sites duty of care they are required to be discharged at an authorised facility. If they are not this could result in prosecution. Where, due to logistical issues or overnight working, this is not possible, the environmental regulator should be contacted to discuss viable alternatives.

Sharps

This is the collective name for needles, syringes and other objects that can cause potential harm if the skin is pierced. If these are found on site do not touch any items and call a specialist contractor to remove them. A registered waste carrier is sufficient to transport sharps waste, with an appropriate PPC or waste management licence in place to allow disposal.

4.5.3.9 Registering premises producing hazardous waste

In England and Wales, there is a legal requirement that the Environment Agency must be notified of premises where more than 500 kg of hazardous waste will be produced in a year. Such sites must be registered with the Environment Agency. Once a site is registered it will be assigned a unique six digit code that needs to be put on all consignment notes. Registration of premises is only applicable in England and Wales and does not apply to premises producing hazardous waste in Northern Ireland or Scotland.

Premises are exempt from the need to register if no more than 500 kg of hazardous waste is produced in a year. However, even where premises are exempt, collections of hazardous waste must still be made by a registered (or exempt) waste carrier,

> Environment Agency hazardous waste producer registration:
> **https://www.gov.uk/hazardous-waste-producer-registration**
> or to apply by post or telephone contact:
> **03708 502 858**

accompanied by a consignment note using a specific exemption code, and transferred to a facility that holds a suitable environmental permit.

4.5.3.10 Disposal of hazardous waste

Assessing waste as hazardous or non-hazardous is a multi-stage process. The flowcharts and supporting text in Environment Agency *et al* (2013) can be used to support this five step process, which includes:

Step 1: determining whether the waste is a 'Directive waste' or is required to be included as a potential hazardous waste based on domestic legislative provisions. Directive wastes are wastes included in the scope of the WFD. In general, nearly all household, commercial and industrial waste is 'directive waste' and as such might be hazardous waste.

Step 2: determine how the waste is coded and classified on the LoW, ie determine if the waste is a 'mirror' or 'absolute' entry on the LoW. If it is an 'absolute' entry then the waste must be treated as hazardous. If the waste is a 'mirror' entry, further classification works (Steps 3 to 5) need to be undertaken to determine whether the waste is hazardous or not. Wastes that do not possess an 'absolute' or 'mirror' entry are classed as non-hazardous or inert wastes.

Step 3 to 5: determine whether hazardous entries are hazardous with regards to the substances in the waste including the determination of:

- dangerous substances in the waste and what their risk phrases are
- hazardous properties H1 to H15 that the waste possess.

Final classification of the waste at Steps 3 to 5 will be dependent on the concentration of substances possessing risk and or hazard phrases. Due to the concentration levels of these substances the waste maybe deemed hazardous waste (see Environment Agency, 2013).

> The information provided in this section is a brief summary to the EA (2013) guide that should be consulted in full when classifying waste. Specialist waste contractors can also help companies through this process.

Many types of hazardous waste can be recycled (eg oil and solvents). Identifying potential recycling and reuse opportunities early will enable hazardous waste to be better managed both in terms of cost control and environmental impact.

Hazardous wastes can be accepted only at a particular hazardous waste landfill if they meet the relevant waste acceptance criteria (WAC) for that class of landfill and the waste acceptance procedures (WAP) are followed.

> A waste carrier and waste recycling company were fined £6000 and £5250 respectively and ordered to pay £5500 costs for dumping construction waste containing asbestos on land near Doncaster, Yorkshire. The landowner was fined £3000 with £5500 costs.

Hazardous waste can also be disposed of via incineration. These plants operate under strict environmental permits so it is important to find out what hazardous waste the plant can accept.

4.5.3.11 Good practice checklists

Planning – SWMP	
Develop a SWMP	
Identify a responsible person for developing, implementing and monitoring SWMP	

Planning – SWMP	✓
Identify and record waste stream (types, quantities)	
Identify and record waste hierarchy options and associated costs	
Review expected waste and disposal options with client, designers and/or architect. Agree actions to reduce expected wastes using the waste hierarchy	
Update SWMP with cost estimates for waste expected	
Define facilities on site for requirements of SWMP	
Ensure sufficient space is allocated on site to meet waste management requirements	
Make a joint commitment to the waste management/SWMP with the client	
Obtain signage for skips and update signs to reflect the site, eg company name, contact details, waste transfer evidence	
Include SWMP requirements into induction material for communication	

Storing waste on site	✓
Segregate waste. Make this easy for site-based staff to do, by providing several waste containers in a designated impermeable waste storage area and briefing staff on their requirements	
Mark waste containers clearly with their intended contents	
Use containers suitable for their contents. Check that containers are not corroded or worn out	
Use covered skips to prevent spread of wind-blown wastes	
Store away from drains and impact	

Storage of hazardous waste	✓
Check that the premises are registered as a producer of hazardous waste, if more than 500 kg is likely to be generated (England and Wales only)	
Ensure hazardous wastes are stored in suitable labelled containers away from sensitive receptors and away from the risk of damage by site traffic	
Hazardous waste must not be mixed with non-hazardous waste	
Do not mix different types of hazardous waste together	
Do not store wastes longer than is necessary to complete documentation to arrange their disposal	

Handling and removing waste (on a confined site)	✓
If removing waste from upper levels on buildings, transport using roller bins	
Store these bins in an area close to lifts	
Arrange for daily collection of bins	
Lower bins to ground floor only shortly before collection lorry arrives.	

Duty of care	✓
Check that a copy of the waste carrier's certificate/environmental permit is available on site and that it is still valid. The waste carrier's certificate/environmental permit should be accepted only if it has been endorsed by the appropriate environmental regulator	
The waste carrier must be certified to carry waste	
The transfer notes should be completed in full and contain an accurate description of the waste, full LoW code, signed by the producer and carrier before waste leaves the site, include SIC code and waste hierarchy declaration	
Keep copies of all waste transfer evidence for waste sent off site for two years for inert and non-hazardous	
Hazardous waste movements must be documented using consignment notes and copies kept for three years	
Carry out spot checks to ensure compliance with the duty of care including: • following the waste carrier to ensure the waste arrives at the agreed disposal site • carrying out periodic assessment and/or audits on the waste carrier • visiting the waste carrier's premises • visiting/assessing agreed disposal site to confirm it is licensed/permitted to accept the waste	

Monitoring and reporting waste	✓
Update SWMP each time waste is removed from site (using transfer and consignment note records)	
Undertake monthly review of performance against action plan including targets and update records	
Report performance internally against action plan and identify opportunities for future improvement	
Complete performance assessment at end of project, including expected against actual waste generated, disposal, cost of disposal and any savings achieved	

4.5.3.12 Further reading

DOENI (2013) *Towards resource management. The Northern Ireland Waste Management Strategy 2006–2020*, Department of the Environment Northern Ireland. Go to: **www.doeni.gov.uk/towards_resource_management.pdf**

DEFRA (2012) *Guidance on the legal definition of waste and its application*, Department for the Environment, Food and Rural Affairs, London. Go to: **http://tinyurl.com/pzmzeu7**

DEFRA (2008) *Non-statutory guidance for site waste management plans*, Department for the Environment, Food and Rural Affairs, London. Go to: **http://tinyurl.com/mh52v8h**

DEFRA (2007) *Waste Strategy for England*, Cm 7086, Department for the Environment, Food and Rural Affairs, London. Go to: **http://tinyurl.com/pe9z7l8**

ENVIRONMENT AGENCY (2010b) *Waste acceptance at landfills. Guidance on waste acceptance procedures and criteria, version 1*, Environment Agency, Bristol. Go to: **http://tinyurl.com/p48sjku**

NATHANAIL, C P, JONES, A, OGDEN, R and ROBERTSON, A (2014) *Asbestos in soil and made ground: a guide to understanding and managing risks*, C733, CIRIA, London (ISBN: 978-0-86017-737-1). Go to: **www.ciria.org**

SCOTTISH GOVERNMENT (2010) *Scotland's Zero Waste Plan*, Scottish Government, Edinburgh (ISBN: 978-0-75598-306-3). Go to: **http://tinyurl.com/q7dkvbq**

SCOTTISH GOVERNMENT (2012) *Duty of care – a code of practice*, Scottish Government, Edinburgh (ISBN: 978-1-78256-138-5). Go to: **http://tinyurl.com/l3k8f6t**

WELSH GOVERNMENT (2010) *Towards zero waste. One Wales: One planet*, Welsh Assembly Government, Cardiff. Go to: **http://tinyurl.com/l8zktzk** (accessed 16 December 2014)

4.5.3.13 Legislation

Legislation is constantly changing, including amendments and new legislation, and this varies between England, Wales, Scotland and Northern Ireland. If site staff are unsure on any environmental issue, contact the regional environmental regulator for advice.

Legislation	Key requirements	Applicable Nation(s)
The Environmental Protection (Duty of Care) (Scotland) Regulations 2014 SSI 4	Requires a transfer note to be signed by the transferor and transferee of waste, specifies information to be included and requires copies to be kept for two years. Includes the use of SIC codes. Enables the use of electronic waste transfer evidence. These Regulations revoke the Environmental Protection (Duty of Care) Regulations 1991.	Scotland

1

2

3

4

Appendices

Legislation	Key requirements	Applicable Nation(s)
Waste Regulations (England and Wales) 2011 (as amended)	Persons concerned with controlled waste are under a duty of care to: • prevent any other person committing the offence of depositing, treating or keeping of controlled waste without an environmental permit or in a manner likely to cause harm to health or the environment • prevent the escape of waste • ensure that waste is transferred to an licensed person or to a person licensed to transport waste • ensure the waste is accompanied by a written description of the waste. From 1 January 2015, an establishment or undertaking that collects waste paper, metal, plastic or glass must take all such measures to ensure separate collection of the waste are available to the establishment or undertaking in that capacity.	England, Wales
Waste (England and Wales) (amendment) Regulations 2014	Clarifies that the transfer of controlled waste may be recorded on alternative documentation, such as invoices, instead of waste transfer evidence and to make other amendments relevant to the registration of waste carriers, brokers and dealers.	England, Wales
Waste (Scotland) Regulations 2012	To provide for the separate collection of dry recyclable waste (ie paper, card, plastic, metal and glass) and food waste, and for the treatment of such wastes and of controlled waste generally from 2014. Operators of a landfill shall not accept separately collected waste from 1 January 2014, or biodegradable municipal waste from 1 January 2021.	Scotland
The Pollution Prevention and Control (Scotland) Regulations 2012 The Pollution Prevention and Control (Northern Ireland) Regulations 2003	Regulates PPC facilities in Scotland and Northern Ireland.	Scotland, Northern Ireland
Producer Responsibility Obligations (Packaging Waste) Regulations 2007 (as amended) Producer Responsibility Obligations (Packaging Waste) Regulations (Northern Ireland) 2007 (as amended)	Apply to all businesses involved in the packaging chain, who handle more than 50 tonnes of packaging material in a year and who have an annual turnover of £2m or more. Also applies mainly to suppliers in the construction industry.	England, Wales, Scotland, Northern Ireland
Waste Electrical and Electronic Equipment (WEEE) Regulations 2006 (as amended)	The WEEE Regulations implement provisions of the European Parliament and Council Directive 2002/96/EC. The Directive aims to prevent WEEE arising, to encourage reuse, recycling and recovery and to improve the environmental performance of all operators involved in the life cycle of electrical and electronic equipment, especially those dealing with WEEE. The Directive sets requirements relating to criteria for the collection, treatment, recycling and recovery of WEEE.	England, Wales, Scotland, Northern Ireland

Legislation	Key requirements	Applicable Nation(s)
List of Wastes (England) Regulations 2005 (as amended) List of Wastes (Wales) Regulations 2005 List of Wastes Regulations (Northern Ireland) 2005 (as amended) The Landfill (Scotland) Amendment Regulations 2003	The appropriate six digit EWC code must accompany waste as a means of classification.	England, Wales, Northern Ireland, Scotland
Hazardous Waste (England and Wales) Regulations 2005 as amended Hazardous Waste (Northern Ireland) Regulations 2005 as amended	No co-disposal or mixing of hazardous waste with other hazardous wastes or non-hazardous waste. Environment Agency/NIEA must be notified of all premises where hazardous wastes are produced above threshold of 500 kg per year. HWCNs must be held for a minimum period of three years Quarterly waste reporting by waste consignee.	England, Wales, Northern Ireland
Waste Management Licensing Regulations (Northern Ireland) 2003 (as amended)	Prohibits the deposit, treatment or storage of controlled waste unless in accordance with a waste management licence. Covers applications for waste management licences, which authorise the deposit, disposal and treatment of controlled waste. Includes conditions on the use of certain mobile plant.	Northern Ireland
The Landfill (England and Wales) Regulations 2002 (as amended) The Landfill (Scotland) Regulations 2003 (as amended) The Landfill (Northern Ireland) Regulations 2003 (as amended)	Regulates landfill sites in England, Wales, Scotland and Northern Ireland.	England, Wales, Scotland, Northern Ireland
The Special Waste (Scotland) Regulations 1996 (as amended)	Defines special wastes and sets out the requirements for disposal of special waste.	Scotland
The Waste Management Licensing Regulations 1994	Prohibits the deposit, treatment or storage of controlled waste unless in accordance with a waste management licence. Relates to persons involved in the collection, storage, treatment and disposal of controlled wastes. The Regulations dictate the licensing of persons or businesses involved in the management of waste and relate directly to the licensing of a site or activity to carry out the management, processing and disposal of wastes.	Scotland
Controlled Waste (Registration of Carriers and Seizure of Vehicles) Regulations 1991	Details the system for seizing vehicles used in the commission of waste offences. Establishes a registration system for carriers of controlled waste and provides for the seizure of vehicles used in waste offences.	England, Wales, Scotland and Northern Ireland

4.5.4   Water consumption

4.5.4.1   Water efficiency

Water is integral to the economy. It is needed for energy production, industrial processes, to grow food and also for construction. In the coming years, the combined effects of climate change and a growing population are likely to put increasing pressure on water supplies and compromise its security.

In simple terms, water efficiency is about completing a task with the minimum amount of water possible. Although, around 70 per cent of the Earth's surface is water covered, about 97 per cent of this is saline and only 2.5 per cent is fresh water. Also, due to the movement of water in the water cycle, much of this becomes locked up as groundwater or in ice caps, meaning that less than one per cent of the water on the planet is readily available for human consumption. So, it is good practice on site to consider water use needs and to aim to reduce these where possible.

4.5.4.2   Water use and waste

It is important to remember that a licence is required from the environmental regulator to be able to attract water for use on a construction site (see **Section 4.7.6**).

So at the early stages of a project it is important to consider the following:

* where water is used
* how much is being used
* where could water potentially be wasted
* what behaviours and/or technologies can be introduced to reduce water use on site.

Many of the key processes and activities for water use on a construction site include:

* site cabins and temporary accommodation
* wet trades
* ground works
* dust suppression
* hydro-demolition
* cleaning
* commissioning/testing of equipment/services.

A small number of contractors have measured water consumption on construction sites for a number of years and the lowest estimate of water use on site for five large companies was 112 m³ per £million contractors output (Waylen *et al*, 2011). Measuring water consumption is the first step towards reducing water use on site. This measuring can help to establish a baseline level and then methods for reducing water use can be implemented.

Once the 'where' and 'how' of water use has been identified, the next priority is to eliminate water waste. However, without this knowledge, it is not possible to determine where water is used and where it has been is wasted. The processes and activities linked to where the majority of water is wasted include:

Strategic Forum for Construction: water toolbox talk:
www.strategicforum.org.uk/ WatertoolboxTalk.pdf

WRAP Water efficiency in construction:
www.wrap.org.uk/content/water-efficiency-construction

Waterwise: **www.waterwise.org.uk**

- dust suppression
- hydro-demolition
- vehicle washdown
- concrete washout
- cleaning
- specialist and high pressure cleaning
- commissioning/testing of equipment/services.

To effectively manage water use on site, four steps should be taken:

1 Evaluate the potential challenges and risks of minimising water use on site.

2 Identify the control and management methods, ie how will it be ensured that water is used efficiently.

3 Adopt an emergency response plan, for example if any issues arise such as leaks or spills.

4 Ensure compliance and monitor consumption, ie ensure compliance with all relevant legislation and that water use is monitored and recorded.

Use of non-potable water (courtesy Willmott Dixon)

4.16

Background

Building a swimming pool demands water in both construction and commissioning, especially because of the leak test. During the construction of Gosport Leisure Centre, the storm drainage was not installed due to the nature of the envelope when heavy rainfalls caused saturation of the ground surrounding the facility.

The team calculated that half of the roof's runoff could be used by diverting rainwater pipes directly into the two pools as part of their construction leak testing. 435 m³ of water was then harvested in the pools and used to identify leaks as well as for site activities, washdown and tool cleaning.

Lessons learnt

This is an example of managing exceptional waterfall and runoff in an effective way.

4.5.4.3 Water reduction

Reducing the use of water on construction sites is a major challenge and will only be successful if these challenges can be overcome:

- **Value for money:** water is a relatively cheap resource and so it is unlikely that the introduction of expensive processes on temporary construction sites will be viable.

- **Work environment:** any technology needs to be robust and able to stand up to the demands of construction sites.

- **Habit:** behavioural change is not a process that happens overnight and so technological innovation or technology that actively influences a behaviour change is likely to be more successful than purely behavioural interventions. A mix of approaches is more likely to be

Figure 4.51 Greywater capture with solar powered pumps (courtesy BAM Nuttall)

successful than considering either behaviour or technology in isolation.

A combination of technological and behavioural change to reduce water consumption can include installation of water efficient fittings (such as dual flush toilets), installing rainwater harvesting systems (**Figure 4.51**), reporting and fixing leaks and/or drips and installing triggers on hoses. Alternatively, use the water hierarchy to evaluate the options (**Figure 4.52**).

4.5.4.4 Water footprinting

Water footprinting is about measuring the total volume of freshwater used to produce goods/products/services and looks at both the direct and indirect water use of a producer or consumer.

Direct water

Direct water use is the organisations use of water, such as for drinking, in cooking and for flushing of toilets.

Indirect water

Indirect use of water is water that is used through the production of products that are then bought or used by the consumer. For example, the amount of water that is required to produce an A4 paper notepad for a person's use would contribute towards that individuals indirect water use.

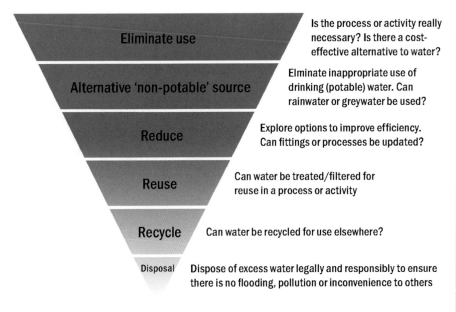

Eliminate use	Is the process or activity really necessary? Is there a cost-effective alternative to water?
Alternative 'non-potable' source	Elminate inappropriate use of drinking (potable) water. Can rainwater or greywater be used?
Reduce	Explore options to improve efficiency. Can fittings or processes be updated?
Reuse	Can water be treated/filtered for reuse in a process or activity
Recycle	Can water be recycled for use elsewhere?
Disposal	Dispose of excess water legally and responsibly to ensure there is no flooding, pollution or inconvenience to others

Figure 4.52   Water hierarchy (courtesy Green Construction Board)

Water footprinting is a form of LCA in that it requires water use across all stages of production to be considered, including the concept of embodied water, and the amount of water used in the extraction, processing, manufacture and transportation of a product.

Imported goods, products or services from abroad contribute towards the water footprint of the country of origin and not the country that the goods, products or services have been imported to. Many countries tend to externalise their water footprint in this way with particularly water intensive products. This puts pressure on water resources in many exporting regions where often mechanisms for wise water governance are not well developed.

Many organisations have traditionally focused upon water use in their operations, ie accounting for abstractions and/or discharges, whereas there should be a focus across the whole of the supply chain.

Water footprinting is quite an advanced topic, and while some footprint studies have been conducted on food and drink products, it is an emerging area in the construction sector.

However, general water efficiency steps can be taken to reduce a projects operational footprint such as by saving water where possible and ensuring that the project does not contribute to any water pollution.

Reducing the water footprint of the supply chain can be done through agreements set to certain standards being put in place. Alternatively, other suppliers could be used, but quite often, looking to improve the water footprint through the supply chain may be a considerable task as it may mean refocusing the business model in order to better control supply chains.

Efforts to increase an organisations transparency could include:

- setting of targets
- labelling products to contain information about the amount of water used in production
- gaining certification through environmental labelling
- informing stakeholders through corporate responsibility reports or other publications.

These are general steps towards improving water efficiency and observing lower water footprints.

The Water Footprint Network

The network is a learning community that aims to connect different groups interested in sustainability, equitability and efficiency of water use.

| Water Footprint Network website WFA tool: **www.waterfootprint.org** | |

The network make data, methods and tools freely available and incorporates perspectives from a broad range of stakeholders from different social, cultural, economic and environmental backgrounds.

Many organisations and industries are now asking for and providing information about the carbon footprint of a product so that labels on packaging and in information brochures have become commonplace. It is forecasted that over the next few years water footprinting will soon be viewed in the same light.

The network provides tools such as a personal water footprint calculator, a water footprint manual (Hoekstra *et al*, 2011) and information about how to calculate a corporate water footprint, water footprints by country and a host of other useful information.

ISO 14046:2014

This Standard covers the principles, requirements and guidelines for carrying out a water footprint and will be used to conduct and report a water footprint assessment.

The water footprint standard is set out to follow the principles of the LCA standards (ISO 14040:2006 and ISO 14044:2006).

It aims to make the conducting of water footprints more mainstream as it is currently a technique in its infancy. To date most product water footprints have been conducted on food and drink products, but now a much broader range of industries are required to conduct water footprints if management of water resources is to become more efficient.

4.5.4.5   Further reading

ISO 14044:2006 *Environmental management. Life cycle assessment. Requirements and guidelines*

ISO 14040:2006 *Environmental management. Life cycle assessment. Principles and framework*

4.5.4.6   Legislation

Legislation is constantly changing, including amendments and new legislation, and this varies between England, Wales, Scotland and Northern Ireland. If site staff are unsure on any environmental issue, contact the regional environmental regulator for advice.

Legislation	Key requirements	Applicable Nation(s)
Water Resources (Abstraction and Impounding) Regulations 2006 (as amended) Water Environment (Controlled Activities) (Scotland) Regulation 2011 Water Abstraction and Impoundment (licensing) Regulations (Northern Ireland) 2006 (as amended)	Makes provision for the licensing of abstraction and impounding of water, including setting limits on the amount of water used.	England, Wales, Scotland, Northern Ireland

4.6   TRAFFIC, TRAVEL MANAGEMENT AND VEHICLE USE

4.6.1   Why is management of traffic and vehicle use important?

There are many good reasons to manage traffic coming to site, on site and when leaving it. Traffic on roads around the site can cause nuisance through noise, exhaust emissions, dust, congestion and mud.

On-site traffic generates emissions, dust, noise and carries risks of damaging materials and causing pollution incidents (eg vehicles damaging oil containers causing ground pollution). Site traffic also forms part of a site's carbon footprint and natural resource use (eg fuel), which can be effectively reduced through good planning.

A good TMP covers all forms of transport, eg road vehicles, pedestrians, bicycles and disabled access.

Emissions

There are two further issues to consider for transport to and from, and on site:

- the effect on local and national air quality
- carbon dioxide emissions.

From a site management perspective these should offer further encouragement for reducing vehicle movements associated with the site.

Also, clients, especially in the public sector, are increasingly requiring the production of carbon footprints for projects, leading to reduction targets.

4.6.2 Traffic management plan

A TMP should enable site-based staff to manage all these risks efficiently and effectively. It should be clearly written and presented, and well communicated to everyone on site including subcontractors, suppliers and site visitors. It is good practice to regularly review the TMP and to make sure that changes to the plan are appropriately communicated.

The TMP should include both off-site (ie travel to/from site, deliveries) and on-site (ie plant/car movements) traffic management requirements.

For details on what information should be included in a site TMP refer to the checklist at the end of this section.

On-site traffic

Plan to reduce nuisance, potential impacts to materials, and polluting substances by:

- planning on-site roads as one-way systems
- including turning circles
- controlling access to and from the site
- adopting and enforcing speed limits
- preparing roads to prevent dust
- ensuring roads avoid fuel and material storage areas
- ensuring delivery and waste removal vehicles are sheeted to prevent dust or material being blown into the air
- minimising drop heights when tipping materials or loading vehicles
- pointing exhausts upwards to disperse pollution and avoid blowing dust up
- communicating to drivers the need to comply with site rules and to maintain vehicles, and the consequences if these requirements are not applied. Also providing training for drivers if necessary

- ensure vehicles enter washing facilities before leaving the site.

Travel Plans offers free help with developing a travel plan: www.travelplans.org.uk

Off-site traffic

Plan the timing of deliveries to avoid vehicles waiting and minimise engine idling. Where several deliveries are likely to take place over a short period, designate queuing areas away from sensitive receptor areas, in liaison with the local authority if on public roads. In urban areas it may be best to allocate a waiting area some distance from the site and then call in deliveries when access to the site is clear.

Figure 4.53   Vehicle leaving site (courtesy Skanska)

Site worker traffic

Site-based staff should not be permitted to park vehicles around the site boundary as this will cause a nuisance to local residents and disruption to deliveries. Arrange designated parking areas when there is appropriate space to do so on larger projects. On more confined sites this may not be possible, so workers should be encouraged to vehicle share, or arrangements should be made for a minibus to collect them from local train or bus stations. Local employees should be encouraged to walk or cycle (ensure that facilities such as secure areas to store bikes during the working day and showers are made available).

4.6.3   Reducing nuisance and congestion around site

It is a good idea to plan traffic movements around a site in consultation with local authorities and the police. It may even be a planning or legal requirement or form part of an agreement with a local authority. This will help to identify both important times to avoid deliveries (eg during school runs) and appropriate delivery routes.

The use of public roads for site access may be restricted. Such restrictions may include:

- weight and width controls
- parking controls
- low-headroom access routes
- accessibility.

Where possible, arrange site access so that all vehicles enter and exit in a forward direction.

RMPs can help reduce the number of deliveries needed and make sure that they arrive at the right time of day. Details of site access routes and delivery times can be included with orders placed with suppliers on a clear map with written instructions.

Encouraging site staff to car-share or use public transport, and/or providing communal transport can further reduce traffic to and from site. Using alternative site transport, such as bicycles, will help reduce dust, emissions and site hazards.

Mud and debris from roads should be cleared regularly and it may be appropriate to install wheel and vehicle washing facilities.

Figure 4.54 *Signage for vehicle routes (courtesy Lend Lease)*

Sustainable TMP (courtesy Jacobs Engineering UK Ltd, and Alun Griffiths (Contractors) Ltd)

Background

Due to the rural nature and location of the A470 site, the transport of site-based staff and materials was a major consideration. It was not possible to transport materials by rail as there was no railhead and it was not practicable to form one. Transport of site-based staff was also difficult by rail due to a limited timetable and difficult connections. The team developed a sustainable TMP that comprised:

● local material suppliers

● a central main compound and localised compounds and laydown areas at major structures

● minibus service to transport site staff from the central compound

● on-site accommodation to prevent commuting

● minimum impact on the existing highways network

● a traffic liaison group to optimise traffic management of the scheme.

Lessons learnt

This is a good example of a comprehensive TMP, developed to limit the impact on the existing transport network and to optimise the traffic management of the scheme.

4.6.4   Good practice checklists

Traffic management plan	✅
Identify sensitive areas (eg schools and homes)	
Plan on-site routes, one-way systems and turning circles	
Use speed limits	
Prepare on-site roads to prevent dust	
Be aware of road restrictions either through road works, narrow roads and bridges with height and/or weight restrictions	
Choose suitable materials for use on access roads – to avoid transferring mud and dust	
Take into account other developments whose activities could affect the project	
Identify suitable locations for parking facilities for private cars and plant	
Ensure there are designated walkways on and around site	
Ensure there are designated vehicular routes on site with speed restrictions	
Locate site entrance and exit so they are not off minor roads	
Gain permission for road closure from the highways division of local authority in smaller scale projects (Highways Agency for larger projects)	
Ensure road closures are carried out by a competent person	
Develop a map showing delivery drivers' routes to site from trunk roads	
Schedule site deliveries outside times of peak traffic volume	
Have designated workers on site to receive deliveries, direct vehicles on and off site, and act as banksmen	
Project vehicles should have badges on their windscreens displaying contact details for the project if they are found to be parked inappropriately	
Offer alternative modes of transport for workers to get to site, eg use of minibuses, car sharing or bicycles	
Identify alternative delivery streams, eg canals and railway if feasible	
Monitor vehicle movements to reduce the likelihood of queuing or causing congestion in and around the local area	
Minimise the need for reversing vehicles (eg one-way systems) and potential nuisance issues from reversing alarms	

Parking	✓
Designate an area on site for site-based staff parking	
Prevent delivery vehicles from queuing outside the site boundary	
Make delivery drivers aware of traffic restrictions on and around the site	

Plant and vehicles	✓
Use a wheel wash for vehicles leaving the site to prevent mud being spread on surrounding roads	
Prohibit vehicle washing outside of any designated area on site	
Use mechanical road sweepers and surface flushing apparatus to clean hard standing and remove any mud or debris deposited by site vehicles on roads, footpaths, gullies or drains near to the site	
Ensure that exhausts do not discharge directly at the ground	
Use retractable sheeted covers to protect wind-blown material	
Ensure all plant and vehicles are in good working order	
Minimise loading and drop heights	
Reverse sirens – consider lorries with 'white noise/broad band' reversing alarms to minimise the effects of noise on local residents	
Should emergency maintenance need to be carried out on site, ensure it is in a designated area away from sensitive receptors and that a spill kit is close to hand	

Delivery schedule	✓
All deliveries to site should keep to their allocated time slot. Failure to do so could mean they are turned away	
No deliveries should be accepted on site without contractor staff to unload them or direct the vehicle	
No materials or rubbish are to be left in the unloading area	
Washout should occur only in designated areas	
All vehicle delivery drivers should wear PPE once inside the delivery area	
Ensure contractors are aware that incorrectly loaded vehicles will not be offloaded	

Site rules for drivers	✓
Access to and from the site will be only via the main entrance gates	
On leaving the site, vehicles are to follow the directions previously given	
All engines to be switched off while waiting to unload	
No parking in residential streets surrounding the site	
All drivers should be asked to proceed with caution particularly at peak school times in the vicinity of local schools	
Drivers should adhere to the site speed limit	
All vehicles entering the site should stop and report to the gateman who will direct them to the required place of loading/unloading	
Avoid the need to reverse where possible, otherwise a competent banksman should be present	
Drivers are asked to park in the designated area and wear appropriate PPE (safety helmet, boots and hi-vis jackets) while away from their vehicles	
All loaded vehicles leaving site should be sheeted – this should be done using a mechanism before entering the wheel wash	
All vehicles should pass through the wheel wash facility and be inspected by the gateman to ensure they are clean before leaving site	
All loaded vehicles leaving site should take the correct documentation with them. Ensure relevant copies of documentation, together with a copy of the weighbridge ticket, are handed to the gateman on return to site	

4.6.5   Legislation

Legislation is constantly changing, including amendments and new legislation, and this varies between England, Wales, Scotland and Northern Ireland. If site staff are unsure on any environmental issue, contact the regional environmental regulator for advice.

Legislation	Key requirements	Applicable Nation(s)
New Roads and Street Works Act 1991	The local authority has a duty to ensure all traffic management and reinstatements are carried out effectively and efficiently to keep disruption to the highway user to a minimum. The council has some powers regarding the timing of street works and the restriction of such works within 12 months of the completion of substantial road works.	England, Wales, Scotland
Roads (Scotland) Act 1984	Ensures, as far as is reasonably practicable, that the highway is kept in a clear and unobstructed condition for the highway user. Anyone contravening the Act is advised accordingly that any obstruction must be removed. Occasionally action may result in legal proceedings against the person contravening the Act.	Scotland

Highways Act 1980	Ensures, as far as is reasonably practicable, that the highway is kept in a clear and unobstructed condition for the highway user. Anyone contravening the Highways Act is advised accordingly that any obstruction must be removed. Action may on occasion result in legal proceedings against the person contravening the Act.	England, Wales
The Street Works (Northern Ireland) Order 1995 (as amended)	A street works licence is required by any person or organisation who wishes to place or retain apparatus in a street, and inspect, maintain, adjust, repair, alter or renew the apparatus, change its position or remove it after, unless the person or organisation has a statutory right to do so. Any person who carries out such works without a street works licence or a statutory right is committing an offence and liable on summary conviction to a fine.	Northern Ireland

4.7 WATER

4.7.1 Why is water management important?

Waters, including rivers, streams, ditches, ponds, lakes/lochs/loughs, groundwater and coastal waters (up to three nautical miles offshore) have legal protection from harm and pollution. Pollution can result from any of the following entering a body of surface or groundwater:

- poisonous, noxious or polluting matter

- waste matter (including silt, cement, concrete, oil, petroleum spirit, chemicals, solvents, sewage and other polluting matter)

- other harmful activities detrimentally affecting the status of a water body.

The status of a water body can be affected not only by chemical pollution, but also by activities directly or indirectly affecting ecology, including changes in physico-chemical parameters such as temperature and turbidity or physical modifications to the hydrology of a water body. For example, activities such as engineering works on inland waters may harm the integrity of the waters or their habitats, such as riverbanks.

It is vital to manage sites properly to protect the water environment and water supplies. If waters are polluted or otherwise harmed, or if unacceptable wastes are discharged to sewer systems, the management, company, subcontractors and clients could end up in court. Also, they may be liable for damages to industries or other third parties using water downstream.

4.7.2 Water pollution

Water regulation applies the PPP, which recognises that the polluter should be financially responsible for costs associated with pollution that arise in terms of human health or harm to the environment. Where there is an imminent threat to the water environment or where damage has already been done, the regulator may require the polluter to implement a number of preventative or remedial measures in response. Failure to comply with the conditions of permits or prevention and remedial obligations may result in a large fine and/or imprisonment.

A site does not need to be next to a river or other water body to cause a problem. Any pollutants getting into subsoil, surface water drain, dry or wet ditch/channel or groundwater can end up in a river even if it is miles away. Often these pollutants can be tracked back to their source.

Even a small amount of material can be a pollutant and one of the most common sources of contamination from construction sites is silt. For example, the normal limits set by the environmental regulator for suspended solids are typically 30–40 mg/l (50 mg/l in Northern Ireland). However, limits can vary dependant on the local circumstances and sensitivities. This is about the equivalent of mixing half a tablespoon of soil in a bath full of water. Another common pollutant from sites is oil. Again, pollution does not necessarily involve large quantities. For example, five litres of oil can cover an area of water equivalent to four football pitches.

High levels of silt can clog the gills of fish and ultimately lead to their death. Also, it can smother invertebrates and sensitive plant life, which are also a food source for fish. When deposited on the bed, silt may prevent fish from spawning successfully and suffocate eggs. Silt levels as low as 15 mg/l can harm juvenile fish.

> During the upgrading of the M74(M) in south-west Scotland, discharges from the construction site into top quality salmonid rivers contained suspended solids concentrations as high as 46 800 mg/l. These high concentrations, derived from silt, resulted in the contractors being fined £40 000 for the offence.

Pollutants can damage the water environment in various ways, as shown in **Table 4.5**.

Table 4.5   *Common water pollutants and their effects on the aquatic environment*

Common pollutants of water	Adverse effect on aquatic environment
Silt	Reduces water quality, clogs fish gills, covers aquatic plants
Bentonite (very fine silt)	Reduces water quality, clogs fish gills, covers aquatic plants
Cement or concrete wash water (highly alkaline)	Changes the chemical balance, is toxic to fish and other wildlife
Detergent	Removes dissolved oxygen, can be toxic to fish and other wildlife
Hydrocarbons, eg oil, diesel	Suffocates aquatic life, damaging other wildlife (eg birds), and to water supplies including industrial abstractions
Sewage	Reduces water quality, is toxic to fish and other wildlife, and damages water supplies

Pollutants that disperse quickly are difficult to control and treat. They are easily transported in waters and the effects are likely to be significant. Some pollutants can smother the surface of watercourses (or standing waters such as lakes or lochs) depleting oxygen and leading to fish deaths or harm to other wildlife or third party interests. Notify and consult for advice the environmental regulator immediately from if spillages occur.

A contractor was found liable for causing oil pollution of the Grand Union Canal after a tap was removed from an oil storage tank. Despite the contractor blaming vandals the Magistrates agreed with the Environment Agency that the site had poor security and the company was fined £7000 and had to pay costs of more than £11 000.

4.7.3 Water pollution prevention

All sites have the potential to pollute watercourses, so a standard approach should be adopted at the earliest stage of the project. Survey the site through a combination of desktop reviews of plans, site drawings, contract documents and reviews of local authority information, and by site walkover for a physical check. Then use the source–pathway–receptor model to identify the site risk as shown in **Table 4.6** (see also **Section 3.2.4**).

Table 4.6   Example source-pathway-receptor model

Source	Pathway	Receptor
Earthworks – silt pollution from vehicle movements	Wash off from roads into surface water drains	Watercourse and aquatic life
Oil storage – leaking on unmade ground	Soil – infiltration	Groundwater

A contractor and client were ordered to pay £21 000 for poor planning and inadequate pollution prevention measures resulting in water offences being committed at a construction development site at Castlewood Grange near South Normanton. Runoff containing debris from the construction process unlawfully entered a nearby Brook, causing a downstream increase in the concentration of suspended solids. The enforcement officers found that the non-existence of a settlement lagoon to treat runoff from the site or a balancing pond were the immediate causes of the polluting incidents.

After undertaking this process the scale and significance of the problem can be assessed and the most suitable control measures for the site can be defined. If following the approach set out in **Table 4.6**, new columns should be added for recording controls and monitoring requirements.

Controls should be applied in a hierarchical manner for each pollution item identified, ie try applying control measures at source, if not possible at pathway, and if not possible at receptor.

When assessing the site for pollution potential, pay particular attention to sources of diffuse pollution. Diffuse pollution is the release of (potential) pollutants from a range of activities that individually may have no effect on the water environment, but at the scale of a catchment can have a significant impact (ie on water quality and wildlife). So, while an individual instance of silt pollution from a site may not have a significant effect, many instances across the site into the same water catchment could be significant.

Pollution prevention control measures

Preventing and managing runoff and silty water

Surface water runoff may cause water management or pollution problems. For example, more than 25 tonnes of sediment can be eroded per hectare off site in a year. Removing the potential for runoff on site should be a high priority. Consider the following:

1   Can the proposal be altered to minimise land clearing and land shaping (ie phased stripping)?

2   Can the proposal be altered to allow permanent stabilisation of disturbed areas as soon as land shaping is complete?

3   Can undisturbed areas be used as sediment buffer zones either during construction or on a long-term basis as appropriate?

4   Can site entry points be located so as to minimise soil contamination of vehicles, and is it possible to allow the early establishment of all-weather parking areas?

5   Is it possible to locate imported material and soil stockpiles in areas that minimise on-site traffic movement?

6   Is it possible to carry out early or phased landscaping to minimise the length of time soils/ground is exposed?

7   Can the works be sequenced to make best use of existing buffer zones and stabilised areas?

8   Can the development be staged so that most of the ground disturbance occurs outside periods of high saturation?

If runoff is still likely to occur, surface water will need to be managed (**Figure 4.55**) so that it does not run into excavations, over disturbed ground, directly into surface water drains/ditches or watercourses, or onto haul roads. Steps should be taken to ensure that the water collection system is adequate to allow for the controlled release of storm flows. Ensure hard standing areas and surface roads are kept clean from mud and oil build-up, and keep stockpiles covered (**Figure 4.56**).

Periods of heavy rain can dramatically increase surface water runoff, giving very high pollutant loads. Some areas of the UK

Figure 4.55   Concrete canvas (courtesy Skanska)

Figure 4.56   *Drainage installation and silt management (courtesy BAM Nuttall)*

are subject to considerably higher rainfall than others, eg west coasts. This factor should be taken into account when considering the management of runoff. Another important factor is soil types on site. Clay soils are much more difficult to remove from site runoff once mobilised than sandy soils. So, construction activities in high rainfall areas with clay soils have the potential to cause more serious environmental harm to waters than projects in low rainfall areas with sandy soils. Issues relating to the potential of pollution from runoff should be fully considered on every site.

Silt fences (**Figure 4.57**) work by preventing runoff flowing over ground. However, it is important not to rely on silt fences to remove sediment from concentrated flows, such as pipe discharges or in flow watercourses. Adequate scour protection (eg rock mattresses, geofabrics) should be provided at points of concentrated discharge to spread flows and reduce velocities, minimising damage and mobilisation of sediment.

Fences cause a physical barrier, capturing the water and enabling it to seep into the ground where it is naturally filtered as it flows downhill. If correctly installed, silt fences can prevent erosion and stop silt laden runoff entering watercourses. Correct installation and maintenance of silt fences is vital. The silt fence should be shaped and installed so that it will catch runoff, without the water flowing underneath or around the edge. Also, the required shape of the silt fence will depend on the gradient of the slope. It is important that the bottom of the geotextile is dug into the ground so that water does not simply flow under the barrier.

Grips, sumps, straw bales and sediment traps can be installed to capture silt. Each of these should be regularly maintained to ensure that they remain effective (ie do not become blocked) and not increase the likelihood of an incident occurring.

Figure 4.57   *Silt fence (courtesy Galliford Try plc)*

Further actions to prevent silty water runoff, include:

- reduce overland flow, eg use of lined (scour protected) cut-off channels to collect and channel water and use of check dams within these
- maintain vegetative buffer zones (10 m min from waterways)
- use of clean aggregate for haul roads
- locate stockpiles a minimum of 10 metres away from waterways
- vegetate stockpiles or cover with geotextiles and use silt fencing
- keep stockpiles on slopes not subject to failure and consider gradient and height accordingly.

Drainage

Identify all drainage on site and use colour coding and symbols to distinguish them, for example blue for surface water, red for foul water and a red 'C' for combined drainage systems. Using the yellow fish symbol beside drains in accordance with the Environment Agency (2012) yellow fish campaign, can also be incorporated to remind people that any waste entering them may go directly to the nearest stream, river, lake, canal, beach or bathing water causing pollution and killing wildlife. This ensures that all those working on the site are aware of the type of drain in the event of a pollution incident.

Depending on the types of drains, where they are on site and potential sources of pollution, control measures can be applied such as placing interceptors in drains to catch oils or placing bunding or silt traps around drains to prevent silt runoff.

Managing effluent from vehicles and boot washing

Where vehicle washing is carried out on site the following measures should be carried out:

- cleaning in a designated bunded area without drains and recycle/treat the water. Disposal of water to sewer may be allowed with the agreement of the sewerage undertaker
- discharge waste water to the foul sewer (with the consent of the sewerage provider)
- collect water in a sealed tank for removal from site by a licensed waste disposal contractor
- use none hazardous and non-solvent based cleaning products where possible
- do not use detergents with oil interceptors as they affect their function.

Vehicle wheels may need to be washed on site to avoid mud on public roads. A specific wheel washing facility (**Figure 3.7**) should be used, with either a discharge to the foul sewer or, if contaminated, collection by tanker. Where a site is not contaminated, water recycling wheel washing systems are available where only the collected silt needs to be removed.

Use of dirt boxes and sedimats to reduce silty runoff on a site with underlying clay ground (courtesy Parsons Brinkerhoff)

4.18

Issue

The project involved constructing a substantial extension to the Hutton Substation in Cumbria, which included culverting a beck and re-profiling a hillside.

The earthworks, which included movements of up to 100 wagons a day, were carried out during a period of prolonged heavy rainfall that resulted in a number of instances of heavily silt-laden runoff reaching the beck. As the underlying ground on site was clay, this did not settle out.

Lessons learnt

The Environment Agency was engaged very early in the project and was consulted regarding measures that could be implemented on site. This proactive engagement and full

Figure 4.58   Dirt box, silt sock and sedimats

transparency with the Environment Agency created trust and good working relationships throughout the project. A system of dirt boxes (Figure 4.58), silt fencing and sedimats were used across the site to try and remove as much silt and colour from the water, which discharged to the beck at the bottom of the site.

A dirt box is a filtration system that uses a 100 micron filtration bag attached to the inlet to remove larger sediment particles and a 40 micron filtration sock or 'silt sock' attached to the outlet to remove finer sediment particles from water.

Additionally, sedimats were used to further filter the water that discharged through the silt socks, along slopes to prevent runoff picking up silt, and within the beck. They proved particularly useful in reducing runoff from exposed ground. Sedimats consist of biodegradable matting whereby sediments within the water flow settle through the upper layer of jute mesh and into a layer of wood wool. A lower layer of hessian prevents the sediment from escaping.

Silt fencing (Figure 4.59) was installed in areas where silty water was likely to runoff the site either into land drains or directly into the beck. As site works progressed, new areas that would benefit from the installation of silt fencing were identified. Similarly, redundant silt fencing was removed where there was no longer a risk.

When carrying out mass earthworks and land re-profiling, ensure landscaping is carried out as soon as possible. Complete landscaping as soon as formation levels are complete in one area before moving onto the next. Ensure landscaping is pre-planned and incorporated into the programme in order to minimise the length of time that large areas of bare ground are exposed.

Figure 4.59   Silt fencing

Facilities should be provided for site staff to wash their boots to remove mud (**Figure 4.60**). This is vital on contaminated sites. Similarly the water should be captured and treated.

Do not allow water containing detergents to enter either surface water drains or other surface water or groundwater bodies.

In exceptional circumstances, discharge to a surface water body may be accepted with the consent of the environmental regulator in the

Figure 4.60   On-site boot wash facility (courtesy Galliford Try plc)

form of an environmental permit. However, this would typically require pre-treatment (for example, silt settlement and oil separation through an interceptor) and it may be difficult to control quality.

If tools and equipment need to be washed, ensure that this is undertaken well away from any waters or surface water drains on a designated collection area to avoid infiltration of potential pollutants into soils.

Boot washers supplied with rainwater (courtesy Lend Lease)

4.19

Background
During winter months construction teams can wash their boots up to four times a day. For a typical £50m construction project, this means about 300 000 litres of mains water consumption per year. To save this volume of water Land Lease is now using boots washers supplied with rainwater that is collected by a harvesting system designed to supply the 70 per cent of the peak demand.

Lessons learnt
Water consumption can be reduced through simple cost-effective strategies.

Managing concrete washout

The washout from a concrete mixing plant and/or from cleaning ready-mix concrete lorries, is contaminated with cement and so is highly alkaline. Do not allow it to enter any surface water drains or other surface water or groundwater bodies.

The preferred option is to wash out the container and chute back at batching plant or in a designated concrete washout area. Where this is not appropriate or possible the following options should be considered for concrete washout areas:

- where possible located away from watercourses and on an impermeable surface
- easily accessible for concrete wagons and situated as close as possible to pours
- stored in secured lined pit (**Figure 4.61**) or container

The hardened residual concrete should be disposed of using the waste hierarchy (see **Section 4.5.3.6**). The options presented in **Section 4.7.6** should be considered for any remaining washout water.

Figure 4.61   Lined washout pit (courtesy BAM Nuttall)

Avoiding spillages

There are many precautions that can be taken to avoid spillages including:

- use of secondary containment, eg bunds around oil storage tanks, double skinned fuel bowsers, drum pallets (for inside/under cover use) that may be a legal requirement
- use of drip trays/plant nappies under mobile plant (**Figure 4.62**)
- supervising all deliveries and refuelling activities
- designate a refuelling area on an impermeable base, away from surface water, away from vehicle movements and appropriately signed

Figure 4.62   Plant nappy (courtesy BAM Nuttall)

- provide secure containment for fuel oil and chemicals, appropriately bunded and consider signing in and out procedures
- provide and identify trained site-based staff to supervise and carry out refuelling training.

Forward or risk planning can ensure a speedy emergency response if things do go wrong. For example, sandbags can be used as a barrier to protect sensitive areas, or to block off drains during refuelling. Also, they are effective for controlling and mopping up some types of spillages. Ensure adequate supply of appropriate spill materials, eg granules, pads, socks and booms. Ensure site-based staff are trained in spill procedures (**Figure 4.63**).

Monitoring

Undertaking the chemical analysis of water samples for trace quantities of particular pollutants is a specialised task. However, the appearance of a sample can indicate potential problems, for example:

- unusual levels of turbidity, colour or dissolved solids

- odour

- presence of oil film.

Figure 4.63   Boom demonstration (courtesy SEPA)

The use of pH testing kits, eg pH meters and test strips, can be used to indicate the presence of specific pollutants on site. For instance, high pH rinse waters from cement batching plants or grouting works can be toxic to aquatic life and may cause a severe pollution incident. This can be identified easily through the use of pH papers that show a colour change in response to differing acidity or alkalinity.

Regular visual checks should be undertaken to check for

- changes in water colour

- changes in water transparency

- oil sheen to the surface of the water

- scum or foam build-up on the surface

- signs of dead plants or animals

- the condition of control measures such as silt fencing.

Monitoring will have to be carried out if conditions are specified in trade effluent consents and discharge permits. This may include monitoring specified limits for flow rate, suspended solids, chemical or biological oxygen demand, or chemical constituents.

4.7.4   Dealing with water pollution – considering the options

To establish the best approach for each site, review the following prioritised options. Those at the top of the list are likely to be least expensive and should minimise the risk of accidental pollution.

Preferred options include:

1 Pump to grassland/field or other soakaway.   **Least expensive**

2 Pump to sewer.

3 Pump to settlement tank, lagoon, constructed pond and/or wetlands.

4 Pass through a filtration system.

5 Use flocculants in conjunction with settlement tank/ponds.

6 Pump into a tanker and dispose of off-site.   **Most expensive**

The preferred options will depend on several factors, including:

- the quantities of water involved
- whether areas are available for storage and treatment
- the level of any charges to be levied by the sewerage provider
- the degree of contamination of the water
- sensitivity, quality and flow of the receiving watercourse
- the characteristics of the sediment
- other users of the receiving water
- ground water table level
- slope gradient
- whether permission/consent can be obtained
- underlying geology (eg clay).

So when making an assessment on the suitability and feasibility for each option, the following information and data should be taken into account:

- size of the construction site
- annual rainfall data
- soil types
- site topography
- surface water flow paths during the various stages of construction
- sensitivity of the waters in, around or connected to the site.

> Obtain the approval of the environmental regulator and/or the landowner before doing anything.

Grasslands/fields or other soakaway

This option is only suitable for water that is unpolluted aside from its silt content and should be conducted well away from excavations to avoid recirculation through the ground. It may be necessary to allow water temperatures to rise by storing in a lagoon before discharge onto crops. Typical infiltration rates are given in **Table 4.7** for various soils.

Pumping to land is the ideal option from excavations, but it needs to be vegetated and adequate space management provided to prevent overland flow. When pumping to grassland it is essential to prevent water logging of ground as this will only result in excessive overland flow and suspended solid loading. This needs to be managed according to prevailing ground conditions, slope and weather. Any discharge to land from pumping needs to be at surface water level and not the base of the excavation as this increases the suspended solid loading.

Table 4.7   *Typical infiltration rates for different soil types (from Bettess, 1996)*

Soil type	Infiltration co-efficient (m/h)
Gravel	10–1000
Sand	0.1–100
Loamy sand	0.01–1
Sandy loam	0.05–0.5
Loam	0.001–0.1
Silt loam	0.0005–0.05
Chalk	0.001–100
Cut-off point for most infiltration drainage systems	0.001
Sandy clay loam	0.001–0.01
Silty clay loam	0.00005–0.0005
Clay	<0.0001
Till	0.00001–0.01
Rock	0.00001–0.1

To get an accurate infiltration rate carry out appropriate measurements, eg using the BRE soakaway test (BRE, 2003).

Sewer

Discharge to the sewer will require consent from the sewage provider. This is unlikely to be allowed in Northern Ireland.

Settlement tanks/lagoons/ponds/wetlands

A settlement lagoon (pond or tank) (Figure 4.64) works by reducing energy and retaining water in an undisturbed state long enough for suspended solids to settle out. The clean water then either flows out at the discharge point or is pumped out. Usually it is necessary to retain the water in the settlement tank for two to three hours at maximum flow rate (Table 4.8). However, finer particulate matter (eg fine sand) may require a longer retention time and possibly larger lagoons. An idea of the required retention time can be obtained by leaving a sample of the contaminated water to stand in a clear glass bottle. Compare this sample to a prepared sample of a concentration equal to the consented/permitted discharge.

As a general rule, when the contaminated water sample looks as clear as the sample representing the consented discharge, it may be discharged. Settlement tanks should only be used with low flow and they are not effective with large volumes.

Settlement lagoons (**Figure 4.64**) are unlikely to be appropriate for water from sites underlain by clay that does not readily settle out. Inspection and maintenance of settlement tanks/lagoons and ponds

Figure 4.64   Settlement lagoon (courtesy Galliford Try plc)

should be conducted on a regular basis. This will help to mitigate the impact of heavy rain on the settlements. The inspection should also cover amphibian checks and areas fenced where appropriate to prevent access (see **Section 4.1.5**).

Where sufficient land is available it may be possible to create a wetland around the pond to allow further treatment of the runoff. Where sustainable drainage systems (SuDS) are to be used for surface water management for the final development, it may be possible to construct such features at the start of the project with the aim of their use during construction (see **Section 4.7.7**).

Table 4.8   Typical dimensions of a settlement tank/lagoon for a three-hour settling time

Pump diameter	Discharge rate (as per discharge permit)	Length	Width
6 in pump	3000 l/min	60 m	20 m
	6000 l/min	80 m	27 m
4 in pump	1000 l/min	30 m	10 m
2500 l/min	2500 l/min	50 m	17 m

Note: assuming one metre deep ponds, where the length = three times the width

Filtration

Discharges with fairly coarse particles (but no other pollutants) and relatively small flows may be treated easily and cheaply by passing them through steel tanks or even skips.

These are filled with a suitable filter, such as fine single size aggregates (5 mm to 10 mm), geotextiles, straw bales or straw bales wrapped in geotextiles. Filtration socks can be added for further treatment. If this solution is used there should be careful control of the discharge quality and

> Consider installing a spare settlement tank/lagoon on site, so that it can be used an as emergency overflow (eg fire water runoff) or when the main tank is being cleaned or in periods of heavy rainfall.
>
> 12

a mechanism to close down the flow. Discharge should then be to land (with landowners permission), to sewer (with water company permission), or to surface waters (with the environmental regulator's permission). Proprietary systems may also be used.

Flocculation

If no alternative treatment is available (whether due to the material characteristics, lack of space or lack of suitable discharge locations), the use of settlement tanks together with flocculants (and/or coagulants) can be an effective solution, particularly to aid the settlement of fine silts. This approach can be expensive and needs specialist advice on the design of the system, the size and dosing rates etc and careful supervision to avoid failures of the system.

Flocculants commonly used include aluminium sulphate and ferric sulphate. If applied incorrectly they can cause pollution and are toxic to fish. Discharges of substances including flocculants/coagulates, to land (with landowners permission and specialist advice), to sewer (with water company permission), or to surface waters (with the environmental regulator's permission) can be made following close supervision and monitoring.

4.7.5   Emergency preparedness and response

All site-based staff should be aware of the appropriate action in the event of an emergency, such as the spillage of potentially polluting substances. A spill response plan/procedure should be developed for the site (see Section 3.4). For details on appropriate fuel storage preparedness measures see Section 4.5.2.6. Any environmental damage to surface water or groundwater must be reported to the environmental regulator unless it can be remedied immediately. Also, steps need be taken to limit the damage caused by any such incidents.

4.7.6   Water abstraction and discharge

If there is a need to abstract water or to discharge to either surface water (eg river, stream, estuary) or groundwater, the environmental regulator should be contacted to confirm whether a PLC will be required (the terminology varies between regions).

Abstracting water

Some construction activities, for example concrete batching or dust suppression, require water to be abstracted from surface water or groundwater.

Abstraction needs to be licensed/permitted because water is a resource and over abstraction, or impeding flows can lead to:

- shortages in water supply
- increased pollution due to the reduced dilution of pollutants
- damage to habitats
- changes to the water regime (eg groundwater draw down) or reduction of levels in water bodies (eg ponds).

Each application is considered for its potential impacts based on national and regional considerations. Contact the environmental regulator for information. The following abstraction limits apply per day:

- **Scotland:** more than 10 m³, register with SEPA. More than 50 m³, licence from SEPA.
- **England:** more than 20 m³, licence from the Environment Agency.
- **Northern Ireland:** between 10 m³ and 20 m³, notify NIEA. More than 20 m³, licence from NIEA.
- **Wales:** more than 20 m³, licence from NRW.

Discharging water

Discharges should only be made to drains following formal legal approval by way of a PLC from the environmental regulator:

- foul water sewer – effluent discharge consent required from the sewerage provider
- waters from surface water drains or any other temporary/permanent outfalls installed to serve the site – discharge consent/permit from the relevant environmental regulator
- discharge to land with the landowner's permission and possibly the environmental regulator.

> A consortium of developers was fined in excess of £26 000 for failing to comply with the terms of their discharge consent and allowing polluted water carrying 10 times the allowable level of ammonia and four times the permissible solids concentration to enter a stream close to their housing development. The investigating officers found that a lack of maintenance of the sewage treatment works (and particularly de-sludging) was a major contributor to the incident and the resulting penalties.

> A developer was fined and ordered to pay in excess of £10 000 for polluting a County Durham stream by discharging extremely polluted water from their site without a discharge consent. The company failed to heed instructions from Northumbrian Water Limited to stop discharging despite being ordered to do so.

If the discharge of water is necessary, discharge to foul sewer should be considered in preference to surface water drains.

Discharge PLCs can be obtained from the environmental regulator, but can take up to four months to obtain, or even longer if there are representations made by third parties/the public. It is important to plan ahead to avoid delays. Even with a PLC, allowable pollution limits will be low.

Water used on site may be contaminated with pollutants that cannot be discharged to the sewer. In these circumstances it will have to be pumped into a tanker or IBC for disposal to an appropriately licensed disposal facility, adding extra costs to the project. **Figure 4.65** outlines the steps to follow when disposing of water on site.

4.7.7 Sustainable drainage systems (SuDS)

Traditional drainage systems could lead to an increased risk of flooding through surface water runoff, to contamination of water bodies with pollutants, or to the diversion of water away from natural groundwater systems. Often, the inclusion of SuDS in a development is a stated policy aim of the environmental regulators for final developments, but also SuDS can be considered for use during the construction phases of projects.

> **susdrain**
>
> An exciting community offering a range of resources for those involve in delivering sustainable drainage systems (SuDS). With the need for SuDS greater than ever before, susdrain provides up to date guidance, information, case studies, videos and discussion forums to help underpin planning, design, approval, construction and maintenance of SuDS.
>
> For more information got to: **www.susdrain.org**

4.7.8 Working over or near to water

PLCs may be required from the environmental regulator and/or local authority for any works over or near to water. Contact the environmental regulator before starting any works in, on or over water to establish requirements. Particular care should be taken to avoid the increased risk of water pollution (**Figure 4.66**). In addition to the measures described in Section 4.7.5, good practice includes:

- ensuring the comprehensive risk assessments to be undertaken, include water-related risks, and that the risk management plans are implemented

- where relevant, use floating platforms such as decks and barges below the works (acting as a bund in case of spillage)

- identifying measures to prevent water reaching a watercourse (eg sandbags, silt fencing)

- availability and, if necessary, use of primary and secondary booms to contain pollutants in the event of substances entering the water erecting dust screens on bridges

- consideration of surface water, groundwater and flood water flows and pathways

- no refuelling within at least 20 m of a watercourse. These activities should be undertaken as far away from the area as possible, on impermeable ground and supervised.

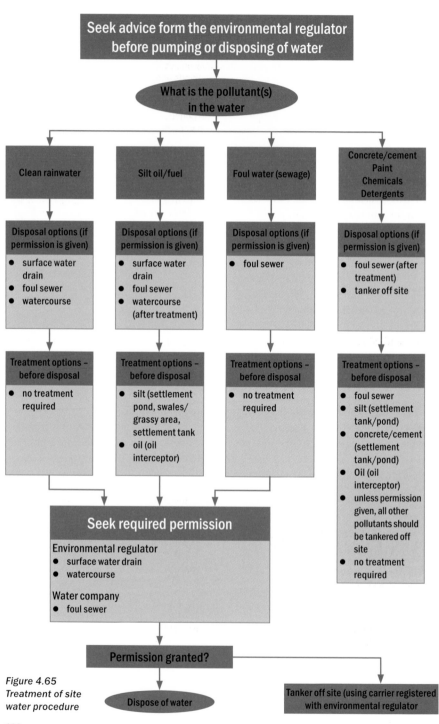

Seek advice form the environmental regulator before pumping or disposing of water

↓

What is the pollutant(s) in the water

Clean rainwater

Disposal options (if permission is given)
- surface water drain
- foul sewer
- watercourse

Treatment options – before disposal
- no treatment required

Silt oil/fuel

Disposal options (if permission is given)
- surface water drain
- foul sewer
- watercourse (after treatment)

Treatment options – before disposal
- silt (settlement pond, swales/grassy area, settlement tank
- oil (oil interceptor)

Foul water (sewage)

Disposal options (if permission is given)
- foul sewer

Treatment options – before disposal
- no treatment required

Concrete/cement Paint Chemicals Detergents

Disposal options (if permission is given)
- foul sewer (after treatment)
- tanker off site

Treatment options – before disposal
- foul sewer
- silt (settlement tank/pond)
- concrete/cement (settlement tank/pond)
- Oil (oil interceptor)
- unless permission given, all other pollutants should be tankered off site
- no treatment required

Seek required permission

Environmental regulator
- surface water drain
- watercourse

Water company
- foul sewer

Permission granted?

Dispose of water

Tanker off site (using carrier registered with environmental regulator

Figure 4.65
Treatment of site
water procedure

Temporary works

In England and Wales, the Environment Agency and NRW and/or local authority need at least seven days' notice of any intention to temporarily or permanently divert the flow of a watercourse, to carry out works over or within a river channel or to begin operations in a river channel.

Obtain approval from the environmental regulator for all temporary works that involve construction, erection, re-erection or modification during works that:

- may interfere with the bed or banks or flood channel of any watercourse
- is within eight metres of the bank of any main river
- is within 16 metres of any tidal defence.

If SuDS are to be used as part of the final development for surface water disposal or management, it may be possible to install ponds and wetlands at the initial phase of construction, allowing site drainage to be managed accordingly. Perhaps following a clean out, the ponds and wetlands can remain on site to serve the development once built.

In south-west Scotland and in Cumbria, ponds were used for the treatment of runoff from the construction of the M74 and the M6. Once construction was completed, the ponds were slightly modified and in some cases wetlands were included. The facilities installed for treating runoff from the construction site were retained as a permanent SuDS feature for treating highway drainage.

In Scotland, SEPA needs to be notified in advance of similar works and depending on the scale of the activity a licence may be required. If the works do require a PLC this can take up to four months to issue and even longer if representations are made by third parties.

In Northern Ireland the NIEA, Rivers Agency and the Department of Culture, Arts and Leisure (DCAL) Inland Fisheries need to be consulted before any river works are started.

Further information can be found in Environment Agency, SEPA, EHSNI (2007) (see Appendix A3).

Figure 4.66   Encapsulation of blasting works (courtesy BAM Nuttall)

4.7.9 Good practice checklists

Know the site	✓
Identify potential pollution pathways and receptors on site	
Define suitable controls to prevent pollution entering pathways and reaching receptors	
Identify temporary drainage patterns on site where cut-off channels and site drainage towards settlement features should be	
Check the annual rainfall data, soil types, site topography and flow paths during the various planned stages of construction	
Identify site drainage as surface, combined or foul water and suitably colour code and mark on the site plan	
Protect/cover drains	
Ensure the correct connections are being made with either foul sewers, surface water drains or combined systems	
Identify all water bodies, gain appropriate consents and put measures in place to fulfil the requirements of the consent	

Managing runoff and silty water	✓
Minimise, where possible, the amount of exposed earth	
Maintain a filter (or buffer strip) strip to protect surface water (minimum of 10 m)	
Regularly check waters for signs of pollution (if applicable)	
Look for any visible signs of discolouration in waters (if applicable) at or near the site	
Silty or discoloured water should not be discharged from the site	
Surface water runoff should not directly enter waters or drains	
Monitor any water treatment methods to ensure their effectiveness	
Inspect scour protection, cut-off channels and settlement features	
If a settlement tank is used, ensure that water is not moving too fast and/or overflowing (other than at the discharge point)	
If necessary, erect silt fences along the downslope or side slope of disturbed areas	
If straw bales, geotextiles or silt curtains are used, ensure they are securely fixed and maintained	
Seed, roll or cover stockpiles as soon as possible	

Managing effluent from washout facilities	✓
Wash out concrete lorries in a suitably contained designated area that is impermeable and/or lined	
Ensure designated washout area is at least 10 m away from drains and waters	
Protect surface water and groundwater from washout	
Put a plan/procedure in place to dispose of washout cost effectively	

Avoiding spillages	✓
Store fuel, oil and chemicals away from drains and water bodies, and in secondary containment in accordance with the appropriate pollution prevention regulations	
Store solvents, chemicals or paints in accordance with their COSHH datasheets and oil storage regulations	
Use drip trays/plant nappies for equipment	
Implement procedures for storage, use, delivery, inspection and monitoring of polluting substances	

Monitoring	✓
Establish a regular monitoring procedure for water discharged from the site and keep records (turbidity/flow rate) in accordance with the PLCs/good practice limits	
Undertake daily visual inspection of watercourses on and near to a site for signs of pollution	
Check outfalls and pipework daily to ensure they are clean and clear of litter	
Monitor and investigate any complaints, incidents and near-miss occurrences	
Monitor bunds and machinery for leaks	
Ensure PPE is in good order	

Dealing with water in excavations	✓
Measures should be put in place to prevent water from entering excavations	
Inform the environmental regulator before undertaking any excavation below the water table, including any site dewatering	
Control water in excavations using stone-filled edge drains leading to sumps	

Dealing with water in excavations	✓
Install cut-off ditches, walls or well point dewatering to manage groundwater flow into excavations	
Obtain a discharge PLC for the disposal of water from excavations where required and monitor	
Ensure water dewatering is disposed of appropriately (ie through a settlement tank, to sewer, to ground or offsite depending on water quality)	

Settlement tank/lagoon/ponds/wetlands	✓
Ensure the size of the tank/lagoon is adequate for the settlement time required and the rate at which water flows or is pumped into it	
Install a long, narrow, shallow settlement lagoon to ensure maximum retention time of all water in the lagoon	
Obtain a PLC to pump clean water from the surface of settlement lagoons into waters or a designated discharge point	
Clean the entry chamber periodically to prevent a build-up of silt	
Regularly inspect/monitor the outflow quality in accordance with the PLC	

Emergency preparedness and response	✓
Ensure site-based staff know who to contact in the event of a spillage, what to do and from where to get equipment	
Ensure appropriate spill kits are available (eg oil only, chemical or general use) and adequately stocked	
Adopt and test an emergency response plan/procedure	
Report environmental damage that cannot be rectified immediately to the environmental regulator and take appropriate steps to remedy the damage caused	
Nominate a spill contractor to deal with major incidents	

Abstracting water	✓
Ensure the site has a PLC to abstract water	
Ensure the site complies with the abstraction PLC	

Discharging water	✓
Check appropriate PLC for disposal of all water are in place, and site staff are aware of the quantity and quality of water that can be discharged	
Check for any visible sign or smell of pollution in waters at, or near the site	
Ensure water is treated effectively before disposal	
If a settlement tank (or lagoon) is being used, check it is working properly	
Supervise and regularly monitor the discharge to ensure compliance with PLCs and general good practice	

Working over or near to water	✓
Avoid storing fuel in containers near water	
Re-fuelling in designated areas only at least 10 m from watercourses	
Ensure that no site works are within 10 m of the edge of waters or ensure a PLC is obtained	
Check that the banks or bed of waters outside the area of the works are not being affected by discharges or vehicle movements	
Spray, dust or other airborne materials should be prevented from entering waters	
Approaches to the watercourse should be kept free from the build-up of mud	
If using a cofferdam to retain water, it needs to be in good condition and working effectively	
Regularly check waters downstream of the works to see if these are silted or discoloured or if there is an oily sheen visible on the water	
Ensure spill kits are adequately stocked	
Site-based staff should be aware of the location of spill kits and know how to use these properly	
Mitigation measures should be put in place in the event of an emergency (eg booms across river). Contact the environmental regulator immediately	
Monitor compliance against any PLCs that may be in place	
Store all fuel oil and chemicals at least 10 m from any water body	
Test emergency procedures regularly	

1

2

3

4

Appendices

Pontoons and barges	✅
All fuel tanks to be secure and safe on the vessel so that there is no chance of collision damage or accidental spillage overboard	
Contaminated bilge water should be pumped to suitable facilities ashore or absorbents used	

4.7.10 Further reading

BETTESS, R (1996) *Infiltration drainage – manual of good practice*, R156, CIRIA, London (ISBN: 978-0-86017-457-8). Go to: **www.ciria.org**

DEFRA (2004) *Groundwater protection code: solvent use and storage*, PB 9849, Department for the Environment, Food and Rural Affairs, London. Go to: **http://tinyurl.com/lcefe4m**

ENVIRONMENT AGENCY (2012) *Yellow fish guidance manual*, Environment Agency, Bristol. Go to: **http://tinyurl.com/n9wpyqz**

MASON, P A, AMIES, H J, SANGARAPILLAI, G, ROSE, G (1997) *Concrete bunds for oil storage tanks*, R163, CIRIA, London (ISBN: 978-0-86017-468-4) (superseded). Go to: **www.ciria.org**

MURNANE, E, HEAP, A, GRIMES, J, RAWLINSON, J, WILLIAMS, J and FORRESTER, L (2002) *Control of water pollution from construction sites – guide to good practice*, SP156, CIRIA, London (ISBN: 978-0-86017-807-1). Go to: **www.ciria.org**

MURNANE, E, HEAP, A and SWAIN, A (2006a) *Control of water pollution from linear construction projects. Technical guidance*, C648, CIRIA, London (ISBN: 978-0-86017-648-0). Go to: **www.ciria.org**

MURNANE, E, HEAP, A and SWAIN, A (2006b) *Control of water pollution from linear construction projects. Site guide*, C649, CIRIA, London (ISBN: 978-0-86017-649-7). Go to: **www.ciria.org**

WALTON, I (2014) *Containment systems for the prevention of pollution*, C736, CIRIA, London (ISBN: 978-0-86017-740-1). Go to: **www.ciria.org**

WAYLEN, C, THORNBACK, J and JONATHAN, G (2011) *Water: An action plan for reducing water usage on construction sites*, Strategic Forum for Construction and the Carbon Trust, UK. Go to: **www.strategicforum.org.uk/pdf/SCTG09-WaterActionPlanFinalCopy.pdf**

WOODS BALLARD, B, KELLAGHER, R, MARTIN, P, JEFFERIES, C, BRAY, R, SHAFFER, P (2007) *The SuDS Manual*, C697, CIRIA, London (ISBN: 978-0-86017-697-8). Go to: **www.ciria.org**

4.7.11 Legislation

Legislation is constantly changing, including amendments and new legislation, and this varies between England, Wales, Scotland and Northern Ireland. If site staff are unsure on any environmental issue contact the regional environmental regulator for advice.

Legislation	Key requirements	Applicable nation(s)
Water Resources Act 1991	It is an offence to cause or knowingly permit any poisonous, noxious or polluting matter or any solid waste matter to enter any controlled waters (including lakes, streams, ponds, rivers and canals).	England, Wales
Water Industry Act 1991 Sewerage (Scotland) Act 1968 Water and Sewerage Services (Northern Ireland) Order 2006	Consent is required from the local sewerage provider before discharging water to any foul water sewer.	England, Wales, Scotland, Northern Ireland
Salmon and Freshwater Fisheries Act 1975 (Modified by Water Resources Act 1991 and Marine and Coastal Access Act 2009)	Covering: ● damage to habitat, spawning grounds or spawning fish ● illegal removal of fish/fishing ● making and maintaining fish passes ● damage and obstruction of fish passes.	England
Water Environment (Controlled Activities) (Scotland) Regulation 2011	In addition to the provisions for licensing of abstraction and impounding water, these Regulations amend the rules governing a number of activities that affect the water environment, including works close to or in watercourses, certain agricultural activities and the storage and use of pesticides.	Scotland
Environmental Permitting Regulations (England and Wales) 2010 as amended	An environmental permit will be required for discharging to water to any controlled water or surface water drain. It will also describe any abstraction limits placed upon a site.	England, Wales
The Environmental Damage (Prevention and Remediation) Regulations 2009 Environmental Damage (Prevention and Remediation) (Wales) Regulations 2009 Environmental Liability (Scotland) Regulations 2009 (as amended) Environmental Liability (Prevention and Remediation) Regulations (Northern Ireland) 2009 (as amended)	If a business carries out an activity that causes environmental damage it will have to remedy the damage. If there is a risk of damage from any business activities, the damage must be prevented. Overall, the Regulations are likely to be used only for the most serious cases of damage. Under the Regulations, environmental damage is: ● damage to surface water or groundwater such that its classification is affected ● contamination of land where there is a significant risk to human health ● damage to EU protected natural habitats and species or damage to SSSIs/ASSIs.	England, Wales, Scotland, Northern Ireland

Legislation	Key requirements	Applicable nation(s)
Water Resources (Abstraction and Impounding) Regulations 2006 (as amended) Water Environment (Controlled Activities) (Scotland) Regulation 2011 Water Abstraction and Impoundment (licensing) Regulations (Northern Ireland) 2006 (as amended)	Makes provision for the licensing of abstraction and impounding of water.	England, Wales, Scotland, Northern Ireland
Water Environment (Oil Storage) (Scotland) Regulations 2006	Where oil is stored in any portable container with a storage capacity of less than 200 litres, the container must be of sufficient strength and structural integrity to ensure that it is unlikely to burst or leak in its ordinary use Where the container has a storage capacity of 200 litres or more, the Regulations require provision of a secondary containment (a bund or drip-tray) to ensure that any leaking or spilt oil cannot enter the water environment	Scotland
Control of Pollution (Oil Storage) (England) Regulations 2001 Control of Pollution (Oil Storage) (Northern Ireland) Regulations 2010 (as amended)	Imposes general requirements for preventing pollution of controlled waters from oil storage, particularly fixed tanks, drums or mobile bowsers. The legislation applies to the storage of 200 litres or more of oil of any kind, including petrol, but excluding the storage of waste oil. Restrictions also govern the use of pumps. It details requirements for oil stored in tanks, drums, mobile browsers or underground that must be identified and implemented, and makes contravention a criminal offence.	England, Northern Ireland

References

ANC (2013) *Green Book: Environmental Noise Measurement Guide (first edition)*, Association of Noise Consultants, St Albans, UK.
Go to: **www.association-of-noise-consultants.co.uk/Publications_Guidelines**

ANDER, E L, CAVE, M R, JOHNSON, C C and PALUMBO-ROE, B (2011) *Normal background concentrations of contaminants in the soils of England: available data and data exploration*. CR/11/145N British Geological Survey, Nottingham, UK (unpublished).
Go to: **www.bgs.ac.uk/gbase/NBCDefraProject.html**

BARBER, B, CARVER, J, HINTON, P and NIXON, T (2008) *Archaeology and development. A good practice guide to managing risk and maximising benefit*, C672, CIRIA, London (ISBN: 978-0-86017-672-5). Go to: **www.ciria.org**

BRE (1996) *The green guide to specification*, Building Research Establishment, UK.
Go to: **www.bre.co.uk/greenguide**

BRE (2003) *Soakaway design* Digest 365, Building Research Establishment, UK.
Go to: **www.brebookshop.com**

BRUNTLAND, G H (1987) *Report of the World Commission on Environment and Development: Our common future*, Oxford University press, UK (ISBN: 978-0-19282-080-8).
Go to: **www.un-documents.net/our-common-future.pdf**

CHARLES, P and WADAMS, G (2012) *Environmental good practice on site – pocket book*, C715, CIRIA, London (ISBN: 978-0-86017-718-0). Go to: **www.ciria.org**

CL:AIRE (2011) *The definition of waste. Development industry code of practice, version 2*, Contaminated Land: Applications in Real Environments, London (ISBN: 978-1-90504-623-2).
Go to: **http://tinyurl.com/oddbo98** (accessed 12 November 2014)

CL:AIRE (2012) *Cluster guide. The definition of waste. Development industry code of practice*, Contaminated Land Applications in Real Environments, London (ISBN: 978-1-90504-617-1).
Go to: **http://tinyurl.com/qgz7a2n** (accessed 18 November 2014)

DEFRA (2006) *Procuring the future, sustainable procurement national action plan: recommendations from the Sustainable Procurement Taskforce*, PB 11710, Department for the Environment, Food and Rural Affairs London. Go to: **http://tinyurl.com/o4duosb** (accessed 10 November 2014)

DEFRA (2011) *Biodiversity 2020: A strategy for England's wildlife and ecosystems services*, Department for the Environment, Food and Rural Affairs, London.
Go to: **http://tinyurl.com/q92x82r** (accessed 16 December 2014)

EA/DEFRA (2004) *Model procedures for the management of land contamination*, Contaminated Land Report (CLR)11, Environment Agency and Department for the Environment, Food and Rural Affairs, London (ISBN: 1-84432-295-5). Go to: **http://tinyurl.com/q6scs6x** (accessed 10 November 2014)

EA, NRW, SEPA, NIEA (2013) *Hazardous waste. Interpretation of the definition and classification of hazardous waste, third edition*, Technical Guidance WM2, Environment Agency, Natural Resources Wales, Scottish Environment Protection Agency, Northern Ireland Environment Agency, UK. Go to: **http://tinyurl.com/o5h6yuj**

EA, SEPA, EHSNI (2007) *Pollution Prevention Guidelines (PPG) 5 Works and maintenance in or near water*, Environment Agency, Scottish Environment Protection Agency, Environment and Heritage Service Northern Ireland. Go to: **http://tinyurl.com/pnoonuh**

EA, NIEA, SEPA (2012) *Pollution Prevention Guidelines (PPG) 6 Working at construction and demolition sites*, Environment Agency, Northern Ireland Environment Agency, Scottish Environment Protection Agency. Go to: **http://tinyurl.com/nand3q4** (accessed 28 November 2014)

ELLEN MCARTHUR FOUNDATION (2012) *Towards the Circular Economy. Volume 1: and economic and business rationale for an accelerated transition*. Go to: **http://tinyurl.com/ot56m4c** (accessed 16 December 2014)

ELLEN MCARTHUR FOUNDATION (2013) *Towards the Circular Economy. Volume 2: opportunities for the consumer goods sector*. Go to: **http://tinyurl.com/a6nnlpv** (accessed 16 December 2014)

ELLEN MCARTHUR FOUNDATON (2014) *Towards the Circular Economy Vol.3: Accelerating the scale-up across global supply chains*. Go to: **http://tinyurl.com/kfz8xer** (accessed 16 December 2014)

HM GOVERNMENT (2013) *Construction 2025. Industrial Strategy: government and industry in partnership*, Department for Business Innovation and Skills, London. Go to: **http://tinyurl.com/nhyttkp** (accessed 16 December 2014)

HOEKSTRA, A Y, CHAPAGAIN, A K, ALDAYA, M M and MEKONNEN, M M (2011) *The water footprint assessment manual. Setting the global standard*, Earthscan, London (ISBN: 978-1-84971-279-8). Go to: **www.waterfootprint.org/downloads/TheWaterFootprintAssessmentManual.pdf**

NEWTON, J, NICHOLSON, B and SAUNDERS, R (2011) *Working with wildlife: guidance for the construction industry*, C691, CIRIA, London (ISBN: 978-0-86017-691-6). Go to: **www.ciria.org**

RUDLAND, D J and JACKSON, S D (2004) *Selection of remedial treatments for contaminated land. A guide to good practice*, C622, CIRIA, London (ISBN: 978-0-86017-622-0). Go to: **www.ciria.org**

SENTENCING COUNCIL (2014) *Environmental offences definitive guideline*, HM Government, London. Go to: **http://tinyurl.com/pcdf7ux**

WAYLEN, C, THORNBACK, J and GARROTT, J (2011) *Water: An action plan for reducing water usage on construction sites*, Strategic Forum for Construction and the Carbon Trust, UK. Go to: **www.strategicforum.org.uk/pdf/SCTG09-WaterActionPlanFinalCopy.pdf**

Statutes

Acts

Clean Air Act 1993 (c.11)

Climate Change Act 2008 (c.27)

Control of Pollution Act 1974 (c.40)

Disused Burial Grounds (Amendment) Act 1981 (c.18)

Equality Act 2010 (c.15)

Nature Conservation (Scotland) Act 2004 (asp 6)

Protection of Badgers Act 1992 (c.51)

Town and Country Planning (Scotland) Act 1997 (c.8)

Weeds Act 1959 (c.54)

Wild Mammals (Protection) Act 1996 (c.3)

Wildlife and Countryside Act 1981 (c.69)

Wildlife and Natural Environment (Scotland) Act 2011 (asp 6)

Directives

Directive 2008/98/EC of the European Parliament and of the Council of 19 November 2008 on waste and repealing certain Directives (the Waste Framework Directive)

Regulations

Conservation of Habitats and Species Regulations 2010 (No.490)

Conservation (Natural Habitats etc) (Amendment) Regulations (Northern Ireland) 2007 (No.345)

Environmental Damage (Prevention and Remediation) Regulations 2009 (No.153)

Environmental Damage (Prevention and Remediation) (Wales) Regulations 2009 (No.995 W81)

Environmental Liability (Scotland) Regulations 2009 (No.266)

The Environmental Liability (Prevention and Remediation) Regulations (Northern Ireland) 2009

Hedgerow Regulations 1997 (No.1160)

Town and Country planning (Environmental Impact Assessment) Regulations 2011

Town and Country Planning (Tree preservation order and Trees in Conservation Areas) (Scotland) Regulations (2010) (No.434)

Town and Country Planning (Tree Preservation) (England) Regulations 2012 (No.605)

British standards

BS 8555:2003 *Environmental management systems. Guide to the phased implementation of an environmental management system including the use of environmental performance evaluation*

BS 1192:2007 *Collaborative production of architectural, engineering and construction information*

BS 5228-1:2009+A1:2014 *Code of practice for noise and vibration control on construction and open sites. Noise*

BS 5837:2012 *Trees in relation to design, demolition and construction. Recommendations*

BS 42020:2013 *Biodiversity. Code of practice for planning and development*

BES 6001 *Responsible sourcing of construction products*

International Standards

BS ISO 14046:2014 *Environmental management. Water footprint. Principles, requirements and guidelines*

BS EN ISO 14001:2015 *Environmental management systems. Requirements with guidance for use*

Orders

The Wildlife (Northern Ireland) Order 1985 (No.171 NI 2)

Noxious Weeds (Northern Ireland) Order 1977 (No.52 NI 1)

A1 UK environmental regulators, nature conservation and heritage bodies

Environmental regulators

Organisation	Responsibilities
UK environmental regulators	Pollution/environmental incident hotline
Contact details T: 0800 80 70 60	
Department of Environment Food and Rural Affairs (Defra)	Policy-maker for all aspects of the environment, rural matters, farming and food production at national level
Contact details T: 03459 33 55 77 / W: www.gov.uk/defra	
Environment Agency	Discharges to land and controlled water, waste, effluent discharges, abstraction licences some nature conservation functions, contaminated land, enforcing environmental legislation
Contact details T: 03708 506 506 / W: www.gov.uk/environment-agency	
Natural Resources Wales (NRW)	Discharges to land and controlled water, waste, effluent discharges, abstraction licences, contaminated land, flood control, fisheries, sustainable development, forestry and forestry regulation, nuclear regulation, enforcing environmental legislation, wildlife conservation authority, designation of sites, sustaining natural beauty, access and recreation, land management of estate.
Contact details T: 0300 065 3000 / W: www.naturalresourceswales.gov.uk	
Scottish Environment Protection Agency (SEPA)	Licensing discharges to the water environment, water abstractions, impoundments and river engineering activities, emissions to air and waste deposits to land. Duties with regards to sustainable development (climate change)
Contact details T: 01786 457 700 / W: www.sepa.org.uk	
Northern Ireland Environment Agency (NIEA)	Discharges to land and controlled water, waste, nature conservation functions, contaminated land and the built heritage
Contact details T: 0845 302 0008 / W: www.doeni.gov.uk/niea	
Local authority	Noise, air quality, traffic, the planning process and contaminated land. Some powers under waste legislation to stop and search waste carriers and confiscate vehicles
Contact details W: www.gov.uk/find-your-local-council	

1

2

3

4

Appendices

Statutory Nature Conservation Organisations (SNCOs)

Organisation	Responsibilities
Natural England	Designated ecological sites, geological and geomorphological sites, and protected species
Contact details T: 0300 060 3900 / W: www.gov.uk/natural-england	
Natural Resources Wales (NRW)	Discharges to land and controlled water, waste, effluent discharges, abstraction licences some nature conservation functions, contaminated land, enforcing environmental legislation, wildlife conservation authority, sustaining natural beauty.
Contact details T: 0300 065 3000 / W: www.naturalresourceswales.gov.uk	
Scottish Natural Heritage (SNH)	Designated ecological sites, geological and geomorphological sites, and protected species
Contact details T: 01463 725 000 / W: www.snh.gov.uk	
Northern Ireland Environment Agency (NIEA)	Discharges to land and controlled water, waste, nature conservation functions, contaminated land and the built heritage
Contact details T: 0845 302 0008 / W: www.doeni.gov.uk/niea/	

Heritage bodies

Organisation	Responsibilities
Historic England	Responsible for protecting historic buildings, landscapes and archaeological sites
Contact details T: 020 7973 3700 / W: www.historicengland.org.uk	
Cadw	Designate archaeological and heritage sites in Wales
Contact details T: 01443 336 000 / W: www.cadw.wales.gov.uk	
Historic Scotland	Safeguarding the nation's built heritage
Contact details T: 0131 668 8600 / W: www.historic-scotland.gov.uk	
Northern Ireland Environment Agency (NIEA)	Responsible for recording, protecting, conserving and promoting built heritage
Contact details T: 0845 302 0008 / W: www.doeni.gov.uk/niea/	

A2 Useful contacts

Organisation	Responsibilities
Chartered Institute of Environmental Health (CIEH)	Maintains and promotes improvements in public and environmental health
Contact details T: 0207 928 6006 / W: www.cieh.org	
CIRIA	CIRIA is the construction industry research and information association. As a neutral, independent, not-for-profit body, we link organisations with common interests and facilitate a range of collaborative activities that help improve the industry.
Contact details T: 0207 549 3300 / W: www.ciria.org	
Green Construction Board	Government and industry initiative working to achieve a low carbon economy. Through a series of Working Groups provides a variety of resources to achieve this.
Contact details W: www.greenconstructionboard.org	
Health & Safety Executive (HSE)	Advice on health and safety issues
Contact details T: 0300 003 1747 / W: www.hse.gov.uk	
National Trust	Responsible for protecting historic buildings, landscapes and archaeological sites
Contact details T: 0844 800 1895 / W: www.nationaltrust.org.uk	
National Trust for Scotland	Responsible for protecting historic buildings, landscapes and archaeological sites
Contact details T: 0844 493 2100 / W: www.nts.org.uk	
NetRegs	Website run by NIEA and SEPA detailing industry sector legislation
Contact details T: 01786 457 700 (SEPA) / W: www.netregs.org.uk	
Resource Efficient Scotland	Scottish Government programme designed to help the public and private sector reduce costs by implementing resource efficiencies in energy, water, raw materials and waste management.
Contact details T: 0808 808 2268 / W: www.resourceefficientscotland.com	
WRAP	Providing expertise, research and practical advice on resource efficiency to Government and industry
Contact details T: 0808 100 2040 / W: www.wrap.org.uk	

Appendices

Organisation	Responsibilities
Zero Waste Scotland	Funded by the Scottish Government to support delivery of its zero waste plan
Contact details T: 01786 433 930 / W: www.zerowastescotland.org.uk	

A3 Regulatory Pollution Prevention Guidance Notes

The Environment Agency, SEPA and the NIEA have produced a range of UK-wide PPGs. Each PPG is targeted at a particular industrial sector or activity and aims to provide advice on legal responsibilities and good environmental practice. Copies of the PPGs can be downloaded from:

- England and Wales: **http://tinyurl.com/mgohzjz**
- Northern Ireland and Scotland: **http://tinyurl.com/la2uskn**

Relevant PPGs and the section of this guide where they are relevant

PPG	Title	Section(s)
1	General guide to the prevention of pollution	4.7
2	Above ground oil storage tanks	4.4.3 4.7
3	Use and design of oil separators in surface water drainage systems	4.7
4	Disposal of sewage where no mains drainage is available	4.7
5	Works and maintenance in or near water	4.7 4.4.1
6	Working at construction and demolition sites	2, 3, 4
7	Refuelling facilities	4.7
13	Vehicle washing and cleaning	4.5.1 4.7
26	Drums and intermediate bulk containers	4.5.1
27	Installation, decommissioning and removal of underground storage tanks	4.5.1

Relevant Welsh Government Technical Advisory Notes (TAN) and the section of this guide where they are relevant:

TAN	Title	Section(s)
5	Nature Conservation and Planning	4.1
10	Tree preservation orders	4.1
11	Noise	4.4.3
15	Development and flood risk	4.7
21	Waste	4.5.3

For more information go to: **http://tinyurl.com/p79unhn**

Relevant Scottish Government Planning Advice Notes (PAN) and the section of this guide where they are relevant

PAN	Title	Section(s)
50	Controlling the environmental effects of surface mineral workings	4.4.1
51	Planning, environmental protection and regulation	4.1
60	Planning for natural heritage	4.2

Copies accessible from: **http://tinyurl.com/7wx7qll**